BUSINESS/SCIENCE/TECHNOLOGY DIVISION
CHICAGO PUBLIC LIBRARY
400 SOUTH STATE STREET
CHICAGO, ILLINOIS 60605

R00163 32601

CHICAGO PUBLIC LIBRARY
HAROLD WASHINGTON LIBRARY CENTER

R0016332601

D1410516

THROUGH RUGGED WAYS

TO THE STARS

SCRIBNERS SCIENTIFIC MEMOIRS

Max Born. *My Life and My Views*
Otto Hahn: A Scientific Autobiography
Harlow Shapley. *Through Rugged Ways to the Stars*

Ad astra per aspera

THROUGH RUGGED WAYS
TO THE STARS

HARLOW SHAPLEY

Charles Scribner's Sons . NEW YORK

QB
36
.549
A3

cop 2

Copyright © 1969 Charles Scribner's Sons

Permission to use some of the illustrative material
in the picture section following page 52 of text has
been received from the publishers indicated below:
The Clarendon Press for the diagram from *The Dimensions
and Structure of the Galaxy* by J. S. Plaskett;
Charles Scribner's Sons for two photographs from
The New Heavens by George Ellery Hale; Yale University
Press for the diagram from *The Inner Metagalaxy* by
Harlow Shapley.
Credits for other photographs are shown with specific
pictures and captions. All other photographs were
supplied by the author.

*This book published simultaneously in the
United States of America and in Canada—
copyright under the Berne Convention*

All rights reserved. No part of this book
may be reproduced in any form without the
permission of Charles Scribner's Sons.

A–3.69 [H]

*Printed in the United States of America
Library of Congress Catalog Card Number 68-57085*

BUSINESS/SCIENCE/TECHNOLOGY

THE CHICAGO PUBLIC LIBRARY

JUN 18 1969   M

R0016332601

BUSINESS/SCIENCE/TECHNOLOGY DIVISION
CHICAGO PUBLIC LIBRARY
400 SOUTH STATE STREET
CHICAGO, ILLINOIS 60605

To the memory of Henry Norris Russell

Ad Astra per Aspera

Half a century ago I was one of a lucky handful of astronomers using the world's most powerful telescope, the brand-new 100-inch reflector on Mount Wilson. Those were rugged times, observing globular clusters by night and ants by day. But they were exciting times, and I soon had some interesting, even revolutionary, results. Though I had a lot of fun with the ants, the studies of the clusters and the structure of our Milky Way are the parts of my work that historians of science find increasingly interesting.

In 1920 I participated in a debate before the National Academy of Sciences on the scale of the universe—a debate that has now become rather famous among astronomers. But except for the text of the debate itself and my technical papers, I had never taken time to write up that affair or some of the other amusing episodes that have occurred on my rugged way to the stars. Thus, when Kenneth Heuer, Science Editor at Scribners, approached me about writing my autobiography I was empty-handed. Besides, quite honestly, I'm too biased to write any proper biography of myself.

Then a happy thought occurred to me. Several years ago, on the back porch of my farm near Sharon, New Hampshire, I had spent two days being interviewed and having this oral history tape-recorded. Although the interviewers missed a few good questions, and although at the time I didn't have any notes or papers to remind me of specific names and dates, the transcription of that occasion could at least provide the basis for a volume of informal reminiscences.

The editorial transformation of the taped interviews to the present book has been nobly performed by Alice Roberts. Of course, I helped a lot, and so did my good wife Martha Betz Shapley. Another valuable collaborator was Owen Gingerich of the Smithsonian and Harvard Observatories, who has read the manuscript in its various forms and who assembled the collections of photographs. Professor Gingerich and his assistant, Barbara Welther, have spent many hours checking facts in the library to make sure that I haven't been too mythological.

I want to thank a number of people who have contributed photographs: Margaret Harwood, Charles A. Federer, Jr., of *Sky and Telescope*, Mildred Shapley Matthews, Helen Wright, and Helen Sawyer Hogg. I also want to thank several persons who have carefully read various sections of my manuscript: Bart J. Bok, now of Steward Observatory in Arizona; Frank Carpenter of the Harvard University Biology Department; Don Price of Harvard's J. F. Kennedy School of Government; Charles Weiner of the American Institute of Physics; John Voss of the American Academy of Arts and Sciences; E. G. Sherburne, Jr., of Science Service; and Howland H. Sargeant of Radio Liberty.

Harlow Shapley

Contents

Illustrations

Chapter One

MISSOURI BOYHOOD

To have had a twin brother was a definite asset of my boyhood. Horace was stronger than I, but I could run faster, so in general I did not lose the fights. We did not have many.

We were named for our grandfathers, Horace Stowell and Harlow Shapley; and although we were not identical twins we had much in common during our early life. Our inspiration and ambition came largely from our older sister Lillian. She insisted that it would be a grand idea for the boys to go to high school and college. So we tried to get ourselves educated.

We lived on a farm about five miles from the little town of Nashville, Missouri, on the edge of the Ozark country. My father did not do much farming; he was a hay producer and hay dealer. We had all kinds of live stock, and we learned about poultry and mules from experimenting. Once a team of mules ran away with me; I was attached to them somehow and was being cruelly dragged. My father ran alongside, pulled out a jackknife, and cut the straps, releasing the mules and releasing me—so we still had a team of mules and a pair of twins.

I suppose ours was a pretty average place. There was not much excitement, except when our uncle, Lloyd Shapley, who was a Navy man, came home with loot from Madeira or Guam. Much later he became governor of Guam. He brought guns into the family in a safe way. I don't know how we managed to survive with so many deadly guns around the place —a Krag-Jorgensen army rifle, three shotguns, and a small rifle. We would shoot at a tree a foot thick and the bullet would go all the way through. It was explained that it would go right through a Japanese also.

One time a neighbor woman went crazy—you could tell the difference; she threatened to murder her invalid husband. There was lots of excitement about that. My father put me on a running pony, gave me a vigorous whip, and told me to ride "hell for leather" for the doctor in Nashville. "Tell him to come prepared to restrain." That poor pony! I got my promised plate of ice cream as a reward.

Nashville is still on the road map. The citizens claim credit for having educated me. But we did not go to a Nashville school, though my father taught there once. Nashville was just where a country store was. We went there at times on horseback—of course we were natural horse riders. But Nashville did not mean much to us. About eight miles away was the town of Jasper, which still has the post office for that immediate region, and about a hundred people. (Fifteen miles northeast is Lamar, Missouri, where Harry S. Truman was born. They admit it proudly.)

We went to the one-room country schoolhouse on the edge of the farm. One year the teacher was our sister; she flattered me once by saying that I was the best student she had ever had. She was grossly prejudiced, of course, and the competition was practically zero. Many of our country teachers really did not know what they were talking about. Our sister finally got both twins briefly to the normal school at Warrensburg, Missouri, but we only stayed a few futile weeks—we ran out of money.

We did not do much reading at home; I don't remember many books in the house. I think we got along pretty well with just self-teaching. Our mother used to read to us from *Three Men in a Boat* by Jerome K. Jerome—very funny and clever. The St. Louis *Globe-Democrat* was our chief contact with the outside world. Most of the few books around were schoolbooks. A Sunday school was maintained briefly at a neighbor's house; our mother got us to go to it a time or two, and there were some pious books in that house. I think it was a Presbyterian Sunday school, although my mother was a "hard-shell Baptist." She was a Baptist only because her father was a Baptist; she wasn't a fundamentalist. Our father also was without religion; the whole family has been without formal religion and has got along pretty well that way. I think that from the very first we were skeptical about the claims of religion and what it would do for you personally. It wasn't pushed down our throats. Our mother wanted the boys to go to the Sunday school, but I think that was more to show off the twins than to have us "get religion."

Our father, Willis Shapley, was something of a leader in the community. My Grandfather Shapley was also politically minded; he ran for State Senator several times and always lost. Republicans had no chance in that Democratic area. The whole family was Republican. My grandmother would be turning in her grave if she knew the twins ever voted Democratic. We were told that all Democrats chewed tobacco. When the twins were only so high, they were taught to say, "Hurray for whoever it was who ran against Grover Cleveland." Even now I wonder about Democrats and tobacco; we were not tobacco-spittin' people.

My father was a paragon of virtue—I don't mean that

too seriously. He insisted that honesty was a very good policy: I don't know that we had a chance to be criminals and have the fun that crime can bring, or is said to bring.

When Horace and I were ten the family bundled up and went by train to visit Grandfather Stowell—our mother's father—at Hamilton, New York. I remember that long trip very well, especially how fearful I was that we'd get lost, or lose our mother. I thought we might lose her at one of the stations where she got out to check the tickets. I always worry.

We lived for one whole year near Hamilton in a lovely stone house that is still there. Now it is a historical monument, labeled with a marker saying that the Stowells once lived there.

In our youth we knew that there was something wrong about the Stowell family. They were hush-hush especially about an ugly old building over the back hill—not in sight of the stone house. What that building was for was never clearly explained. Some would say that Uncle Joe—a mysterious Negro—had lived there. Many years later, our sister told us that it had been one of the stations of the underground railway.

Our grandfather was a rabid abolitionist and was associated with well-known people of the pre-Civil War days in smuggling Negroes from the South up to Canada, and that old house was one of the stopovers. The Negroes would travel at night. Of course that human smuggling was over long before we were born. It was kept secret because it was illegal to ship Negroes, and Grandfather Stowell was breaking the law—not that anybody bothered him very much. It just was not very respectable to do a thing like that; but Grandfather was a man of firm convictions and an Abolitionist with a capital A. Now we are proud to say that the house has been marked by the New York State Historical Society as a place where Horace Stowell ran a Negro-smuggling business. Perhaps I inherited something that showed up when I brought Jews, *et al.*, to America in the Hitler days and fought Senator Joseph McCarthy and his crew in the 1950s. I always have been a bit obstreperous!

I don't know why we went to Hamilton that year—maybe just to get away from Missouri. I never thought to ask at the time. The information came down to the twins that we were going, and we got on a train. The trip was very exciting for ten-year-olds. My father came later with two or three carloads of western horses. That made quite an impression. The twins would show off by riding the horses while standing up, especially if people from the Sunday school were watching. After we got out of sight we sat down.

In New York State we also went to a country school; it is now called "Shapley School." A building in Barton County, Missouri—a quarter of a mile from the home place—is also called the Shapley School, but it is practically dead. The one in the middle of New York State is very sturdy; I think it may be kept as a monument, if we behave ourselves properly. Grandfather Stowell is buried nearby on the edge of the Colgate University campus.

That year of New York schooling was a little different from our schooling in Missouri, but I'm afraid the twins have overemphasized the difference. I don't believe the teacher was especially good. I remember she spanked me once and I didn't think that was justified—I claim that the other fellow was the guilty one.

We didn't have very much of a wild life in New York

State and so were glad to go back to Missouri to the guns and the hunting—to hunt rabbits and squirrels. We weren't very good shots, any of us, but at least we went through the form of playing Wild West hunters. There's a good deal of play acting in me, it seems—it shows up later in this book. As we had rather large meadows, we had nice prairie fires, and we could futilely hunt for mythical prairie chickens.

Early adventures are inevitable around a farm or in a small town. For instance, I once pulled a playmate out of deep water when he was going down for the traditionally fatal third time (which is a fraud, I think). Later I won a swimming race and damn near perished from exhaustion. Both these experiences were in a mine-pit. There was a creek on our Missouri farm and a nice little river, the Chenango, ran through the New York State place where we visited Grandfather Stowell. We had a number of experiences, as boys always do around water where they are swimming and diving and getting hurt and having all sorts of excitement. It was just typical farm life. We had chums in the neighborhood, and we would go to see them and go swimming or horseriding. It was not an unhappy childhood, although at the time we did not know that it was happy. One catches on to that with age.

We were all full of romance—you might say of mythology. My twin brother and I used to get together and spin yarns. He would be the audience and I would be the voice. We would develop imaginary episodes; we called it "talking a story." These were heroic tales, more like Paul Bunyan stories than romance from a feminine standpoint. We did not rescue fair damsels; we did heroic things—fighting bulls, shooting bears, and all such imaginary dramas, or doing something to surprise our father (or our mother, who was never much surprised at anything). I think it was because we did not have many books that the "talking stories" played such a considerable part in our lives over a number of years. We couldn't get our younger brother, John, the realist, involved in these stories very much; but Horace ate them up and enjoyed the imagination that went with them. I thought this was an unusual thing to do, and we were rather ashamed of it. Later I found it is not at all uncommon. My friend Hudson Hoagland of the Worcester Foundation for Experimental Biology, whom I have known since the early Harvard days, admitted to me once that he "told" such fanciful stories to his sister. "I was so ashamed, but now that you confess, I admit that I 'talked' also."

I didn't realize it at the time, but I think "talking stories" made it easier for me to write rapidly later when for a time I was a newspaper reporter. I could write pretty well—I wrote fast and rather accurately. That ability stayed with me for a long while, but later I seemed to lose it. I think my feeling for writing was partly inspired by my sister; I know she was herself ambitious to write. My uncle Lloyd, the naval man, was also a sort of inspiration, but not too much because of his work with the Navy—we were nonmilitaristic.

When I was about fifteen, I went to Pittsburg, Kansas, to a sort of business school. After a few months, I had that finished off, and I became a newspaper reporter—a crime reporter on the *Daily Sun* in Chanute, Kansas, a tough oil town nearby. I had the kind of experiences there that a reporter would have in such a town, especially if he were agile and got around. One little affair was on election night. There were a lot of drunken oil men on the streets. I set about to protect the office, thinking they might start something there. A policeman came along and there was what we called a duel; two men shot each other and one of them died. I handled that story at age sixteen. It was sort of dramatic for those times, before we had wars and horrible things became common.

Another time we were having a political scramble, and my newspaper took one view and another newspaper took another view, and so we shot off a good deal of strong language. The worst politician pushed me out of his office and went on talking to others inside. I sat down outside his office and wrote down in shorthand all that was being said. (I had learned shorthand at Pittsburg.) We just printed verbatim his rough statements—four-letter words and all. Consequently he wanted to murder me and blow up everybody. It was rather spectacular. For we did the proper thing—we made and printed a picture of my shorthand. Anybody who knew my kind of shorthand could read it. Of course, there was no guarantee that we hadn't forged it all. It was a rather live bit of country journalism for those times. Our man won!

From Chanute I went to Joplin, Missouri, where for a while I was police reporter on the Joplin *Times*, a miserable little daily. Joplin was worse than Chanute; it was a lead-zinc town and there were many tough characters, usually hanging around police headquarters. My newspaper life was not very long—less than two years—and it was not very dramatic. It was also a long way from William Allen White's type of rural philosophy.

Chanute had one of those Carnegie libraries, which was the first public library to cross my path. I also took some of my few pennies and sent away for one or two books—I had to get them from Chicago. I began reading history then, and

Tolstoi and Dostoevski—my first serious reading. I was fascinated by Dostoevski. I wonder now whether I was just showing off by reading such things, but of course they were readable. We did have some books of poetry at home, and poetry you could recite while milking a cow and keep the rhythm going. I used to recite Tennyson, and we also had a book of poems by Nathaniel Willis. I think my father was named Willis because somebody in the family liked that book—it was one of the few books around the place.

Poetry is still one of my weaknesses. We now have two or three shelves of poetry. I have given a lecture on poetry more than once. It is a light-hearted lecture—"Science and Poetry," starting with Job and coming up through Lucretius and Dante and Tennyson to the modern humorists like David McCord and Morris Bishop. In the past twenty years I have not perpetrated any poetry of my own, but I have repaired a few poems that needed repair—such as where Tennyson in *Maud* refers to a "sad astrology"; he meant astronomy. I have not found the answer to why he did that, but some other errors I do have answers for. I mean to write an article one of these days about science and poetry with special reference to *Maud*. Tennyson was a very deep and brilliant thinker; I like to play with him.

My newspaper jobs in Chanute and Joplin I took to earn money, because I had suddenly got the ambition to do what my sister wanted the Shapley boys to do—try to go to college. She was then the mistress of a one-room schoolhouse in Montana, and she knew her way about. I also greatly admired the boys who came home for Christmas holidays from the colleges of Kansas.

When my younger brother John and I decided "to get

educated," we first thought we should get some high school "learning." "We'd better see if we can get admitted to high school." John was fairly bright and I was very industrious, and we had an ambitious mother. Her great ambition was that the boys "should amount to something, get somewhere, go to school." Once when the family seemed about to strike a little zinc and lead (it petered out pretty soon), my mother's main hope was that it would pan out well because "then the boys could go to college."

I remember that pathetic hope of hers because she was still around applauding when we had been to many colleges and had earned many college degrees, and three college presidencies had been pointed my way.

Well, how to start? We had to do something vigorous. We went down to the elegant high school at Carthage, Missouri, about twenty miles from where we lived, and asked if we could start in the second semester. I was about seventeen or eighteen at the time. But when John and I asked to be admitted to Carthage High School they turned us down. They said, "No, you aren't qualified." Forty years later they celebrated Harlow Shapley Day with much noise. I am probably the only astronomer who was refused admission to a high school. I was brave in those days. I said, "What about this Carthage Collegiate Institute down the street?" We went down the street about three blocks to the Carthage Collegiate Institute, a Presbyterian outfit. It was quite willing to take the little money we could afford. So we became students, and I graduated from there in 1907 on just two semesters of residence. But I took numerous special examinations.

I was valedictorian of my class—it was a class of three! My essay, which I ran onto one time since, was on "the romantic values in Elizabethan poetry," or something like that. It was pretentious, but it helped get me into the University of Missouri.

Between semesters Horace and I went off on a cheap excursion to New Orleans. We had quite a few experiences, including two mild train wrecks and a fire. The railroad paid us to be quiet about the wrecks—that was one source of funds for my college tuition.

I also worked between semesters on the Joplin *Times* and worked some on the farm. As far as I can remember, the only time my father complimented me was when he said that I was better on a hay wagon than anybody he had ever hired.

I memorized Latin and geometry on the hay wagon—a rather unusual place to study. And I learned my Greek— what little I've now forgotten—out in Montana in similar circumstances. That studying was aimed at getting me admitted to the University of Missouri. Because my early schooling was so sketchy I had to pass many examinations and get many high marks. To get those marks, I had to flatter the teachers (and they were glad to be flattered). And so the time came when I went to the University, in Columbia, Missouri, a couple of hundred miles from home. From then on I was never stopped; the vanity probably helped.

Chapter Two

FROM JOURNALISM TO
ASTRONOMY

I went to Missouri University with about two hundred dollars, and there I struck a snag. I had supposed I was going to study journalism. That had been my goal and my plan, and I had done a little studying toward it during the summer. But when I got to Columbia I found that the opening of the much-advertised school of journalism had been put off for another year.

That School of Journalism has now become famous; Walter Williams was its first dean. But it did not open the year I arrived at the University.

So there I was, all dressed up for a university education and nowhere to go. "I'll show them" must have been my feeling. I opened the catalogue of courses and got a further humiliation. The very first course offered was a-r-c-h-a-e-o-l-o-g-y, and I couldn't pronounce it! (Though I did know roughly what it was about.)

I turned over a page and saw a-s-t-r-o-n-o-m-y; I could pronounce that—and here I am!

From then on things went swimmingly—I had found my field. After two years Professor Frederick H. Seares, the head of the astronomy department, put me in charge of the first-year course. Astronomy was one of the snap courses for liberal arts students. I still remember my first meeting with that class. I walked in and was confronted by fifteen or twenty giggly sorority girls. They had a lot of fun teasing me. I asked them to write their names on slips of paper. When I handed out the slips my hands rattled. I was scared to death. The next time I had a student pass out the slips, and that was the last time in my life that I was frightened by girls.

Pretty soon I was a real member of the astronomy department. In those days Missouri University had a 7½-inch telescope with a Clark lens. I used it to make a few observations of variable stars. We had a very bad photometer—I would swear at it, even now, if I knew how to swear at photometers. But it was a stellar photometer, and I used it.

We did a little spherical astronomy—practical astronomy we called it. We went outdoors with the instruments and measured the altitude of the sun, or moon. There was an old meridian instrument on hand; we put in much of our time trying to correct it. We got some of our education by finding faults in the instruments. The equipment was small, but it was a complete observatory—the Laws Observatory, named for Professor S. S. Laws, once the president of the University.

The University was not as rigid in the matter of credits as it became in later times. There was pretty much of a free distribution. As I remember it, you took the courses you wanted. I wanted a second course in astronomy, and that was all I got. We used a textbook in practical astronomy that Seares had written, and one in general astronomy. But there was a good deal of private discussion in our education—sitting around and fighting it out with Seares.

Seares was a pretty good teacher; by pedagogic standards, I think he could be called a good teacher. He suspected that I might have some qualifications. He was a very prim sort of person and very neat.

At that time Eli S. Haynes was Seares' assistant; then Seares left and Haynes was in charge. I was second to him.

Then I took my A.B. degree in 1910. I think I was the only astronomy major at the time, though the University had been offering a degree in astronomy for eight or ten years. Seares had been there most of that time. I didn't know anything about him when I came to the University except that he was the man who was teaching astronomy. He left the University to go to Mount Wilson Observatory, where he later became editor of the publications and was very demanding about the accuracy of measurements. Probably his greatest contribution was his editing of the Mount Wilson papers. He would encourage me occasionally by saying, "That's well done." That was the most anybody ever got out of him.

Another man on the staff at Missouri University who had a lot of influence on what I could do and did do was Professor Oliver Kellogg, a mathematician. He thought he saw in me some spark of mathematical ability. He was wrong, but he backed me up when I took various courses in mathematics.

In physics I practically flunked the first semester. I skipped first-year physics and took the second-year course. It was pretty tough on me. After the first test, the instructor sent for me and suggested that I drop out. That of course annoyed me. In the first place, I showed that they had not read my exam paper correctly, and that on another answer I was not wrong.

Then I pitched in—I wasn't going to be thrown out that way. When I graduated two years later I took "high honors" (so labeled) in mathematics and physics—the only one in my class who did.

Of course, I did not have any real preparation for the advanced work I got into at the University, though my sister's tutoring helped, and so did my writing ability and the newspaper experience. I had not had any science at all, and my only mathematics was algebra and geometry which I had been taught by my sister and by a playboy cousin who had explained at the same time that plane geometry is nonsense.

There was no instruction in natural history in the country schools I attended. I turned over rocks and saw some little crawling things called ants—I used to look to see if they had guests with them, such as beetles or butterflies; they do sometimes. We did not learn much of anything in country school, but we were pretty good at tracking a possum at midnight and roasting him over an open fire; we learned some ordinary natural history from doing things like that.

I was flower-sensitive, but that was partly because of the applause that my sister and mother gave my efforts; my interest was not deep. I didn't know there were elementary books on botany. I liked to walk in the woods, as I do at the present time, but the region around Dublin, New Hampshire, is glacier country and richer in botanical excitement than a southwest Missouri farm was.

As I look back on it, I always had a wide curiosity, but not much then for natural history. The biology of the barnyard is a thing that naturally affects all boys of twelve or so, but to me it was sort of revolting.

Among my University teachers I remember best a man named A. H. R. Fairchild who taught us Shakespeare's *Henry V;* it was one of the most beautiful presentations to a bunch of half-awake students I ever saw. I still read that play with a thrill, more than any other except perhaps *Hamlet.* Another teacher who stood out was a French teacher, who gave me a double A, or whatever was tops and beyond. At that time I couldn't make mistakes in French. Now I can; I've learned how to do that since. I may have learned some French from my Grandmother Shapley, who lived with us sometimes; she spoke French a little.

My teachers of mathematics in college, besides Professor Kellogg, were Louis Silverman, Earl Hedrick, and others who were rather distinguished. Another outstanding teacher at the University was in classics, Dean John C. Jones. This reminds me of an episode almost worth recording. I had learned Latin rather quickly on the hay wagon and I was able to write Latin verse correctly. That's something of a stunt; I don't know that it was a qualification for anything in the future—probably not. Anyway I was good enough in Latin as a senior so that when they were putting an honorary degree on me about fifteen years later, Dean Jones, who was the man who had to stand up, apologize, and put the hood on me, whispered during the ceremony, "Shapley, I think you should have gone on with your Latin." Then he draped a degree in science on me. He did not think much of the science honor.

If Seares had not set me to work that first year (at 35 cents an hour), I might have gone into classics. Until then, and for quite a while after that, I thought I would, because I found classics, especially Lucretius, very fascinating. As I have often said, Lucretius was a great scientist; his *De Rerum Natura* is the greatest scientific poem ever written. In fact, while I was still in the University I wrote an article on Lucretius and it was published. That was my first published science paper. It was printed in *Popular Astronomy*, a magazine published in Northfield, Minnesota. The magazine also published another paper of mine about the same time. I sent them still another one on a heavier mathematical theme, and they turned it down. That ended my early career as a science writer.

I did not have any special interest in the stars before I went to college. I remember only one incident; it happened one summer when my father was managing a hay ranch somewhere and the twins were helping a bit—not much. He told us that according to the St. Louis *Globe-Democrat* there was going to be a shower of shooting stars on a certain night. It would be after midnight: "Why don't you stay up and see them?" He himself wasn't going to stay up, but at least he encouraged us to. So we lay down on our backs on a beautiful August night to wait for the first ones to come, and we both went soundly to sleep and never saw those Perseids.

That was my first contact with astronomy.

It may seem strange that, with no experience or particular interest in astronomy, I went on to make a career of it, at a time when the prospects for a degree were not very promising. The explanation is, I think, that when I got to the University I found—and I know it was a genuine finding—that all fields of learning are exciting. I came very close to accepting a classics scholarship that would have given me a chance to be a classicist. Perhaps I couldn't have got excited about physics, but about astronomy I could and I did.

Mathematics I also found exciting—differential equations especially. I apparently did something brand-new in Fourier's series. Kellogg thought, and said, "This is a marked man." He was going to have the idea published sometime, but he never did, and I didn't want him to because I didn't understand what I had done. But the excitement was there.

I never went back to journalism, although my two or three close friends in college were journalists. I didn't even work on the college paper, though I am a little surprised that they didn't get me, hardened journalist that I was.

After I had been two years at the University, Fred Cone, the editor of the Chanute, Kansas, *Daily Sun* came over to Columbia and offered me a one-third interest in the paper if I would come back and be the managing editor. It was a rather nice offer, but I was brave enough, or foolish enough, to say, "No, I want to stay here."

He said, "All right. You're going to grow up here and sit around in fat chairs and eat bonbons. You don't want to take the rough and tumble of police reporting any more."

I tried to tell him about astronomy, but I did not get anywhere. He took the first available train home. He was offering me a one-third interest in not much—and I never had much regret about the decision.

In fact, I had learned pretty early how dishonest journalism can be. You don't readily expose the scandals about the best advertiser. You cover up the faults of the sinners. One of my jobs in the journalism field had been to expose a mathematical horse. A circus was taking money from us yokels to see a horse solve equations. My boss on the Joplin *Times* sent me to see this sideshow. I guess he gave me a quarter to get in. He could not afford much more than that. He said, "Go and see if you can find out what this racket is, and tell me what it is. I think the man is a crook. You may see through it and then we'll talk to their advertising agent and maybe they'll change their minds and advertise in the *Times*." So I went. I was sixteen or seventeen and moral, you might say. I went out to the circus and stood around, and soon I solved the problem.

It was a stupid-looking horse. A bunch of bums were around it. On the concealed signal of one of the men in the audience, the horse would start to paw the ground. On a signal from the master he would stop. That was all there was to it. The answer came through the horse's pawing. . . . "How much is two and two?" He pawed four times and we were amazed. The audience could not do much better than that. "How much is four and one?" "Five." Correct. "Three and three?" "Six." Correct.

Then I got smart and asked, "What is the square root of four?" They promptly gave me the bum's rush—"Get out of here, boy. This is for men."

The *Times* got the advertising, and my story was dropped.

That experience got me interested in "psychics," and I have had many dealings with them since. All I have known are frauds.

I didn't really amount to much in the University. I was fairly good at tennis until I banged my elbow on the tennis net post and never got over it. I don't know whether I would have made the team or not, but anyway it was interesting. I still follow the tennis of others.

Campus social life did not concern me very much. I'm afraid we studied rather seriously. After the first year my chum and I boarded in a dormitory where after the evening meal we all went upstairs and danced for a while. That was a sort of social affair, but it was mostly men dancing with men. The summer schools were livelier, and we had more fun. I got some of my extra credits by going to summer school.

Then, in my third year, I met a brunette named Martha Betz, from Kansas City, Missouri, and never got loose, or wanted to. We first met in a mathematics class—she sat in the front row and knew all the answers. She was a clever lady in those days. She took five full courses and got the top mark in all five. Her field was philology and German literature and such things. Eventually it became astronomy, and she has published quite a few astronomical papers.

Later, while I was at Princeton and was studying hard on the orbits of double stars for my doctoral thesis on binaries, she was a graduate student at Bryn Mawr. "Listen," I said, "I'm a busy man. If you want any more letters from me you will have to write my language." She already had more languages than I had. I wrote down something squiggly, maybe something sentimental. "What language is this?" I asked. She looked at it for a bit and then went home and learned shorthand. She learned her shorthand quickly from me. We have corresponded in the Gregg system ever since. All our letters, which are very frequent, are in Gregg shorthand. (I once wrote to Mr. Gregg himself in shorthand, and he replied in longhand.)

I was at Missouri University four years altogether and in that time earned my bachelor's and master's degrees. I also taught elementary astronomy during my last two years. My timing was accelerated because I took summer work. Then also there was at Missouri, and now also elsewhere, a scheme in which the number of credit units you receive for a course depends on your standing in the class. The plan is not very good. It limits the fields that a student is exposed to. It kept me from knowing anything about chemistry, for instance. I collected too early all the credits I needed to graduate. All the chemistry I had was gathered in a few weeks in a summer session. I got the top mark in the course and thought I knew chemistry, so I didn't study it any more. I have kicked myself ever since, because chemistry is what I want to know. I even think of studying it at the present time. I have become wise in a way, chemically, but I did not have what I should have had. I was cheated out of it just because I was too darned bright that one summer.

While I was getting my master's degree Professor Kellogg heard that the Thaw Fellowship in astronomy at Princeton was open. "Let's make a try for it," said he. So we did. If I had had a fellowship in mathematics to shoot at, just for financial reasons I might have gone on with that, although I never really had a good instinct for mathematics. Some of my family had the feeling, and Mrs. Shapley is a good instinctive mathematician. Just as I gave up journalism because the opening of that school was delayed, I went to Princeton because the fellowship was open and I got it. And in getting that, I got some people to say nice things.

Henry Norris Russell, under whom I worked at Princeton, was amazed after a bit that I could do what I could do. (Since the fellowship was handed out by mail, I did not meet him until I got there.) He was enthusiastic about having a graduate student who could go along with him in the analysis of eclipsing binaries. He often used to say: "I had this struggle with darkening at the limb of an eclipsing binary. All these observations had to be worked over; it looked hopeless, and then the good Lord sent me Harlow Shapley."

My family was very proud when I received the big Princeton fellowship. My sister was living in the West by that time and stayed out there. My father was naturally quiet. He was like that. He would not say anything one way or the other, but we knew that secretly he was proud, and we found that he even boasted a little. My mother of course thought that I was on the way to the presidency of the United States.

My twin brother Horace did not go in for higher education. He went to Warrensburg State Normal School for a bit and that was all. He went West and stayed there a long time, doing various things. He gradually bought most of our shares of the home place and paid off the mortages. That was his ambition—to do as his dad had done.

Our Grandfather Shapley had a lot of land assigned to him as part of the pay for fighting in the Civil War. He was a colonel when he finished. From New York State he had gone to a county in the northern tier of the counties of Illinois, but he wasn't there very long. In Missouri, a great deal of land was handed out, and he got it one way or another. He was "land poor." He owned about a square mile at the place where Shapleys are now. Horace has bought almost all the land that was in the original holding and is living on rents—a good job if you can get it.

Horace is also a rather prominent citizen of his community at the present time. He lives alone in the house where the family lived a hundred years ago, but he associates with the neighbors a great deal. To my surprise, he is a churchman, among other things; he goes to Sunday school and argues philosophically with the preachers. And he is a sort of Santa Claus to the community.

For the past three or four years he has been taking extension courses at the University of Missouri. He drives thirty miles to his classes and gets good marks in the courses, which are mostly in the social sciences. He is getting his college education in his eighties.

Chapter Three

WORKING WITH RUSSELL

In the fall of 1911, after a summer visit to my mother and sister in Kalispell, Montana, I went to Princeton to take up the fellowship. As soon as I knew I had it, I began spending the money. It amounted to $1,000, which was pretty good in those days—the largest fellowship Princeton offered. I did not have to pay any tuition, and I got a room in the observatory free, or for very little. So the money amounted to something nice—I could get along on it and even make one trip back home.

Soon after I arrived I met Professor Henry Norris Russell; it was a strange meeting. Russell was a very shy man, and he had to meet this unknown graduate student that Missourians spoke well of. The first day Russell asked me to come with him and Robert Williams Wood of Johns Hopkins—the famous Robert Wood—to look through the 23-inch telescope for sulphur deposits on the moon. Russell was a high-class Long Island clergyman's son and very high hat.

"Mr. Shapley, perhaps you would open the door for us?" he would say. Mr. Shapley did open the door. He didn't like it! I don't quite know what was expected. Perhaps he thought I would kowtow to him, which I suppose I did to some extent; he intimated that I was, after all, a wild Missourian of whom no one should expect much.

But that attitude lasted only a little while. In a few days I came to him with an orbit I had solved by a method that he had used. That woke him up, and pretty soon we were the chummiest of creatures. Students were much interested when Shapley, the Missourian, and Russell, swinging a cane, would stroll across the campus. If students got in the way, Russell would just brush them off with the cane. We got along well, and we both learned a great deal.

I discovered I had really passed muster with Russell when he told me where you could find fringed gentians north of town. When he revealed that secret, I knew I had arrived.

Russell first went to Princeton in 1905 and became the director of the observatory in 1912. He was eight years older than I. We remained intimate friends, talking over our troubles together and discussing scientific matters, up to the day when I stood bareheaded in his front yard as they brought his body home from the hospital to the study where we had so often bravely speculated.

The other astronomer in the department was Raymond Smith Dugan. He was good, but he was slow compared to the scintillating Russell. He was an assistant professor and naturally was overshadowed by Russell, which he knew, but he was a faithful routine observer of eclipsing stars. He was also interested in the wild flowers of the community and taught me about them. I went on playing around with botany to the extent that I now have identified 121 species of flowers on my New Hampshire farm. Most botanists haven't done that much.

When Dugan died, after I had become director of the Harvard Observatory, I went down to the funeral. Of course the director of an observatory is expected to do that kind of thing; but before I went to the house where the funeral was being held, I went out along the shores of Lake Carnegie and picked a handful of wild flowers of different kinds. I brought them up and put them on the coffin. That made a tremendous impression, which I didn't expect; to me it was just a sentimental recognition of our past together.

Most of my time at Princeton was spent on my thesis and on other work with Russell. I took very few formal courses. I took one astronomy course given by Russell, which was a sitting-around-the-table type of course. I went to lectures, and I eavesdropped on paleontology with William Berryman Scott—"Bill Geology Scott"—because it is such a fascinating subject.

When I come back in another incarnation I intend to be a paleontologist. Or else I want to be something big like those beasts of the Cretaceous period that have now disappeared. Of course I may not come back—that would be just my luck—or if I do I may then be the spotted heifer of Bangalore or something of that kind.

I took one regular course in mathematics and one in philosophy, a course in optics with O. M. Stewart, and a course in physiology. The last was not exactly relevant, but physiology is another subject that fascinates me—that is the reason for my interest in ants, which I will describe later.

I also developed an interest in music at Princeton. At home we had an organ and my mother was a pretty good organist, though she gave it up later. At Missouri University we did not have much access to music, but at Princeton the graduate students were struggling to "get culture." The graduate school, under pretty good leadership, encouraged students to take advantage of New York City and the culture there. A trip fifty miles from Princeton to New York to hear an opera was something that we indulged in a bit—not often because it cost too much money. After the opera we would go home and talk about it. We also went to hear symphonies, and chamber orchestras came to Princeton. I remember even now some of the music and singers that came to Princeton. But I had one horrible experience. A string quartet was playing beautifully a Brahms piece. I was in the gallery. I got to thinking dreamily of the past at the University of Missouri and specifically of a time when Eli Haynes came into the observatory office and instead of putting his hat down on the typewriter and using the spittoon, did it the other way around. He spit on his typewriter and . . . It was such a comical thing that while this soft Brahms music was gliding on, I suddenly remembered how Haynes' eyes bugged. I burst out, "Ha, Ha, Ha!" Then I nearly died of humiliation.

At Princeton there were some interesting colloquia; Owen Willans Richardson, who later went back to England, talked about photoelectricity. He and Karl T. Compton, who became president of Massachusetts Institute of Technology, were working together. Richardson was a quiet person; very few people knew him. I did only because I pushed myself on him to find out what Compton was up to and see if I could learn from it. Richardson had a genius for finding the errors in Compton's work, just by pointing to the equations. "Have you checked that this really is a sigma square?" He was a quick-minded person but his was not a very attractive personality, or maybe he didn't want to cater to me. He won the Nobel Prize in 1928 for his work on thermionic phenomena.

My work with Russell was mostly on the orbits of eclipsing binaries. That was to have been a simple thesis but it soon got beyond thesis size. What was important in those years was learning the tools for working with variable stars—that, and my association with Russell. He could do the mathematical calculation so rapidly I despaired of keeping up with him. He would come over to my desk, glance at my calculations, and then walk up and down the room in excitement. "By golly, it worked out," he would say. "The formula works!"

I showed him everything I did, and we would talk it all over. Of course I did a good deal of reading, too—partly because Russell seemed to read everything. But probably two-thirds of my time at Princeton was spent on the research project. Of that time about two-thirds was given to the mathematical calculations, and a third or less to observing with the telescope. The climate wouldn't permit any more observing.

The work started with a paper that Russell had written before I came to Princeton. In the meantime many new observations had come out; also the 23-inch telescope at Princeton was found suitable for doing the photometric work. I worked night and day, happily, with slide rules and mathematical tables. (Not long ago one of those bright-eyed lovely visitors who want to flatter me asked: "Dr. Shapley, is what they say true—that you measured the size of the universe with a twelve-inch slide rule?" "No," I said. "That's a damn lie! I used a ten-inch.")

An eclipsing star is one for which the light first seems steady, then dips down a while, then comes back. The dipping is the eclipse. From the shape of the "light curve" we could deduce a number of things: one was the orbital period; another was the inclination of the orbit. But the main reason we worked on eclipsing binaries was that we could get their mean densities. It was a nice trick. All this has been described in some of my many papers. Aristotle had only the light of a star and its position to deal with, but I know of more than twenty different facts that can be learned by studying the eclipsing double stars with a spectroscope and an accurate photometer. The Greeks were handicapped by not having our instruments. I wish they had had them; we would be further along now.

The calculations got more and more exciting as we began to realize something of the sizes of the stars and the distances involved. Here were nearly a hundred stars whose sizes were enormous compared to the sun. The sun has a density of 1.4; some of these stars have densities only one-millionth of that—enormous gas bags.

My desire, almost from the first, was to get distances. Isaac Newton and others had looked deeply into the sky, but they could not tell how far out in space a certain star is, though Newton made some guesses about Sirius. But the last column in the big table of my orbital work gives some estimates of the distances for eclipsing binaries. It was guesswork in a way because we did not have much material, but it did show one thing that surprised us—Russell and Dugan and me—and that was that the distances were pretty darned big. We knew that we could get the distance of Sirius, 8 light-years away, by trigonometry and we might with a lot of work get distances up to 50 light-years with some security, but not much.

I gave a colloquium or two in the physics department, where I sprang some new ideas. It bothered Russell when I came out with ideas that he had not known about; I got criticized kindly for that. As far as I can remember, the new ideas had to do with getting the distances of eclipsing binaries from studies of their colors and spectra—a forerunner of the theories on Cepheid variable stars that are described later. This work on binaries was my first attempt to find out where we are in the universe.

At the time, of course, I had no real concept of what kind of universe we live in or what the galaxy is like, and I did very little good thinking on the subject. But a little later I made two diagrams that really stunned me—one on the center of the Milky Way and the other on the distance of NGC 7006, a globular cluster. The first revised the size of the universe; the second pointed toward its center.

As I mentioned earlier, Russell had started the work on eclipsing variable stars a year or so before I went to Princeton. Probably the reason he said, "The good Lord sent me Harlow Shapley," was that I could do the dirty work with the little calculating machines we then used. (Now of course we push buttons; it is a different technique.) Russell had worked on only one or two easy stars, and his method had not been a very good one. Actually there were no traditional methods. Until Russell and Shapley came along there had been practically no eclipsing-star workers.

One of the reasons I got such a kick out of the work was that it pleased Russell so much. I remember how satisfied I was when he would come in and I would say, "Here I've laid out another corpse for you to look at." He would go over to the "plot" and make buzzing noises, and then walk up and down, he was so excited about it. Those were happy days for him—and for me.

It was obvious from the first that I had found a sort of gold mine when I began to work on eclipsing variable stars. The field had not been worked very much, and Russell and I had new methods of analysis.

By the end of 1912 I was beginning to publish papers on

this subject, some with Russell on darkening at the limb for eclipsing variables. Except for a note or two published in *Astronomische Nachrichten* about the time I left Missouri to go to Princeton, these were my first technical astronomical papers. When my first hard scientific paper was published, I am sure I strutted around. I would "accidentally" leave it where somebody would see it.

At Missouri I had done some observing with a bad photometer, but at Princeton we had a bigger telescope, and I did quite a bit of observing of eclipsing binaries and also made an analysis of the published material from all over the world. The final publication of the work on eclipsing binaries, which was my Princeton thesis, came after I had gone to Mount Wilson, but the dissertation was completed and accepted in 1912 and published in 1913 in volume 36 of the *Astrophysical Journal* which was the prestigious journal of the time. The complete work, Princeton Publication No. 3, was published in 1914 as a quarto volume; the so-called thesis was really an abstract of that volume. It dominated its field for some time. The publications on eclipsing binaries in the Princeton period made a considerable impression; it was acknowledged that I was getting somewhere with eclipsing stars.

I read a paper at a meeting of the American Astronomical Society in Pittsburgh in 1912. That was the first astronomical meeting I attended. I had tried to make my own lantern slides, but when I saw how professional the other astronomers' slides looked, I forfeited my lunch money to have my own set made up by experts.

By the time I went to Mount Wilson I had published a dozen papers. One or two were rather significant; others were small. Curiously enough there were not many duds; in fact there were hardly any that I would say now I should not have done.

Within a year after I went to Mount Wilson I published a paper, Mount Wilson Contributions 92, "On the Nature and Cause of Cepheid Variation," which showed that the stars called Cepheid variables are single stars and not doubles. After proper incubation I hatched what we have since called the pulsation hypothesis of Cepheid variation, and that hypothesis is still being used. It has been enlarged in some ways, but it was a good hunch.

The Cepheid variable star analysis was a laborious paper, half footnotes nearly. It is interesting that at that time I should have so much to say and could say it concretely. The proposal was that the Cepheid variable stars are single stars that are throbbing or vibrating masses of gas. To get that far, I had to drop the earlier idea that the Cepheid variable is a double star.

After I had published the paper I worried about whether I might have taken the theory from Russell. He and I discussed it. I claimed that I had taken it from him, and I was going to write an apology. It seemed preposterous that a professor would have a student who would snitch his good ideas. But Russell said he had never heard of the theory, and anyway he was doubtful that it was correct. But it was; it stands up—it is, in fact, basic in astrophysics.

All this made me confident that I could do something significant at Mount Wilson if the people there gave me a chance. And they did give me the chance. Working on eclipsing stars for two or three years made me grow in maturity rather rapidly. I realized that I could do things other people could not or would not do, and therefore I was useful. When Russell and I joined in the paper on darkening at the limb for eclipsing binaries, and I worked out some of it independently of him, I began to feel that maybe I was on my way. During the Princeton days it seemed to me that I had a future in astronomy—in fact, a rather easy one, and maybe, if things turned out all right, even a happy one.

As a graduate student at Princeton, I began looking toward the future. I wandered around a bit. About 1914 I went up to Harvard, stopping along the way like a student visiting places. I stopped at Yale and at Brown University. Brown offered me a job, which I turned down. I think the people there knew I would not take it, but at least they went through the form, because I was Russell's student and did not have a job.

On the visit to Harvard three things happened that affected my future a good deal. One was that I had dinner with the famous and jolly Miss Annie J. Cannon. She was a josher in a way, and charming. "Young man," she said, "I know what you're going to do. You're going to be the director of the Harvard Observatory." Then she laughed. She remembered it ten years later when I became that director. I asked her how she had managed it. Again she laughed.

Another episode involved E. C. Pickering, then the Harvard director and at that time the most famous American astronomer except possibly George Ellery Hale of Mount Wilson. He said to me, "Anything in the observatory that you want, especially these photometer observations that Oliver Wendell made before he died—just help yourself." He invited me to his home to dinner, and we sat in those famous tall chairs. I was terribly impressed with the great man that he was, and with the chairs. He set flute music up on a music stand and just sight-read it. He was impressive-looking too, in a large way. That was my first contact with Pickering.

The third incident was that I went to call on Solon I. Bailey, upstairs by the observatory dome. He was later acting director of the Observatory in the interim between E. C. Pickering and myself. Bailey was pious and kind, a wonderful sort of man, but so New England it made you ache. He said, "I hoped you wanted to come up here; I have been wanting to ask you to do something. We hear that you are going to Mount Wilson. When you get there, why don't you use the big telescope to make measures of stars in globular clusters?"

In 1913, after my thesis had been accepted, I went to Europe. My younger brother John and I went together, and I spent five months traveling around. I don't remember exactly how I got the money for the trip—honestly, I hope. I think my father sent me $200, or both of us together got $200, and I had saved from my munificent fellowship—the $1000 a year. We went steerage, and lived cheaply, as students do and should.

John and I happily parted company in Italy after a few weeks. He was interested in art and archaeology and wanted to look at churches in Ravenna, while I wanted to go to observatories. John stayed in Europe to study. He took his doctor's degree in Vienna and became a considerable scholar in his field—linguistics, archaeology, history of art. He taught at New York University until he was stolen away by Robert M. Hutchins for the University of Chicago. After he retired he taught at the Catholic University of America, then went to Baghdad for three years. He still lectures part time at Howard University.

After we separated I went to observatories and some astronomy meetings. I had already had a good deal of correspondence with Europeans about variable stars. Also I carried a botany book with me, and when, while walking, I came to a new town, I would identify the plants and make a list of them. I made a guide to Europe as seen by an amateur botanist. It was pleasant. The European flora is a good deal like that of New England, not like that I had known in the Ozarks or that I knew later in California.

I got as far east as Hungary, as far north as Sweden, as far south as Algiers. I went to England, too, and Ireland. In England I went to a meeting of the Royal Astronomical Society, where I met almost everybody of stature.

I met Ejnar Hertzsprung on that trip, at a meeting of the Astronomische Gesellshaft in Bonn. That Dane was one of the best astronomers Europe has produced. He did most of his work at Potsdam and later was at Leyden. He had the brightest ideas but failed to develop many of them. I also met Karl Schwarzschild, the father of our Princeton astronomer, a man who was so much like George Ellery Hale in his genial personality that I later would frequently confuse them.

My travels were marred by one tragic shock. After I left my brother in Italy I came up from the south to Paris for the first time. I had already gone around to the north—to Sweden, Holland, Germany, Belgium, and so on. When I reached Paris I found a telegram awaiting me: my father had been killed by lightning. That soured me on Paris so keenly that I never wanted to go back. I wandered the Parisian streets for a long while in shock and blind mourning. Neither my mother's death nor my sister's affected me in the same way as the sudden death of my father, for whom we had a great deal of respect although there had not been very much close association.

After the European jaunt I went back to Princeton to finish details of my doctor's thesis. In those days Princeton did not have qualifying examinations, language examinations, course requirements, or anything like that—very loose management, compared with today. I couldn't then have passed the examinations I have since given many times to Harvard students: ours were tough; the students had to know something about all astronomy. But at Princeton the thesis was the thing, and mine was considered rather outstanding.

I did have one oral examination with Russell, Dugan, and two deans. They quizzed me deeply. There were four examiners. I went in feeling cocky, sure that they would ask the promised easy questions, and the rascals didn't. It was a mean oral. I did miserably. I could have talked intimately about at least a dozen stars, but Dugan asked, "How would you adjust a photographic telescope?" I shall never forget my failure on that. Dugan's account of that oral is somewhat different from mine—but in any tongue it smelled!

But they gave me the degree anyway—*magna cum laude*. I think it was the first doctoral degree under Russell. In a way I traded for that degree. I said to them, "Give me the degree and I will go on and do twenty additional orbits and the thesis will be better—it will be something you will not be ashamed of."

One of my fellow students at Princeton was John Quincy Stewart, who was younger than I. He had a brilliant idea that was not fully recognized by the faculty. He became unhappy about it and felt that he had been robbed by all of us, so he went into "social physics." I don't know what that means, but that was the title of his work; he got a grant from the Rockefeller Foundation for the study. I believe it had to do with the distribution of populations. Even Russell couldn't understand it.

As I was approaching the thesis finish, I wrote Professor Seares at Mount Wilson Observatory and asked him about a job. He wrote back: "I think we can fix that all right." Before long he made a date for me to meet the great George Ellery Hale, who was the founder of almost everything astronomical and was the director of Mount Wilson Observatory.

It was a remarkable meeting. I went from Princeton to New York in time to stay overnight restfully, and I saw two operas. One was *Pagliacci*; the other was *Versiegelt* by Leo Blech. The next morning I had breakfast with Seares and Hale, who were on their way to Europe. Hale asked me what I had done the night before, and I told him about the operas. He was very much interested and made good critical remarks. I have checked one or two of them since and found them not too correct, but he showed much interest. We talked at length. Then, unexpectedly, he said, "Well, I must be going."

Not one word had been said about astronomy or about my going to Mount Wilson, or anything like that. He had met me, and we had chatted about something neither of us knew much about. Then he went away.

I didn't know what this meant. Had my table manners slipped up? (Once my uncle gave me a gun for my good table manners!) I said to Seares, "I don't quite understand this. Have I done something wrong?"

"Oh no, no, don't worry about that," Seares said. I think he was sadistically enjoying the whole affair. He later explained that Mr. Hale knew that I would know astronomy, perhaps more astronomy than he did, and that I had the Princeton touch. When he found that I seemed to be a decent guy, that was all he wanted to know. He did not want to know about orbits of eclipsing stars, with which I was filled to the brim. So he just walked out on me.

Then, not long afterward, I got a letter. It said: "Please come to Mount Wilson."

Chapter Four

FINDING THE CENTER OF
THE MILKY WAY

On the way west from Princeton to Mount Wilson (and the magnificent salary of $90 a month) I stopped in Kansas City and took on a wife. She had been at Bryn Mawr and went home ahead of me for clothes and such. We were married on April 15, 1914, and went on to California—by train, of course, in those days. It was a long trip, but I had some nice observations with me, and we worked on the orbits of eclipsing binaries on the honeymoon. Mrs. Shapley was very quick at computing, so we enjoyed ourselves for a couple of days.

The authorities had not known that I was bringing a wife along, but they did not disapprove. One of our first jobs was to look for a place to live in Pasadena. We found a place on Villa Street, about a block and a half from the observatory office and shops. I was to go up the mountain and use the 60-inch telescope for three or four days once a month. That arrangement persisted for quite a while.

At the time I arrived, Hale was still director but was not often around. He was already ill; he had had a nervous breakdown in 1913. I went to see Hale early for an embarrassing reason. I thought I was not getting as much pay as I should have been getting. It turned out to be an oversight, so I got upped from $90 a month to $135. I liked to point out immodestly to beginners I employed: "When I was your size they paid me $90 a month and I was already internationally famous!" The low salary was because the Mount Wilson people had expected me to be living free on the mountain.

Hale did not like my approach, and I did not like having to mention the subject. But nobody else was going to look after me, and I wanted three meals a day. They played fair with me after that—very fair. When I was called finally to Harvard, after an interval of some years, I was the highest-paid astronomer in America. I was getting about twice what the Astronomer Royal was paid. Astronomers came cheap in those days!

I began work officially the day I arrived. I was told at once what my job would be: to help Seares with observations on the colors and magnitudes of stars. What he was doing made sense, but it didn't turn out very happily because of the limitations of the 60-inch reflector, and I don't think he was satisfied. But he worked hard, and I did. They told me that as soon as I learned how to handle the 60-inch telescope I would have lone access to it. I worked for Seares on photometry for about a year, but I could mix in some work on globular clusters and variables and Cepheid variables.

I was the first of a group of five or six, including Adrian van Maanen, Edwin P. Hubble, and Roscoe Sanford, that came to Mount Wilson at that time or a little later.

When I first went up on the mountain, Charles St. John was there looking for water; he believed in water witching. People get funny ideas at high altitudes. Ferdinand Ellerman, Walter S. Adams, who came with Hale from Yerkes Observatory, Arthur King, and George W. Ritchey, who was there for optical work, were also on Mount Wilson. That was practically all—Alfred H. Joy came later.

I enjoyed observing with the 60-inch telescope, especially the novelty of using such a big instrument. It was wonderful that a beginner could have such machinery. Later F. G. Pease and I began the experimental work with the 100-inch—and that I liked. But observing was always very hard work for me. I "suffered" quite a bit those long, cold nights. I suppose I didn't get as much sleep in the daytime as I needed, for I was running around observing ants in the bushes. For three or four years observing was rather tough going. But it was tough going for the others, too. Scientific research is laborious, especially if you work all night. Now they break the nights sometimes, but in those early days everybody worked through the dark hours. Also they now have electrically insulated suits, which makes a big difference.

We had to be rugged in those days. We would go up the mountain, a nine-mile hike, sometimes pushing a burro, sometimes not. The new road had not been put in. Adams was acting director during Hale's illness, and he could take on anything. He was a tough one. He was our best tennis player and best billiard shooter and best mountaineer. He held us down—not very openly, but he would let word get around that some person didn't seem to observe so well when the night was really cold.

Adams was not a slave driver; he was an operator—an inspirer, in a way. He drove himself and expected others to do the same thing. He was not a good loser in anything, but being so good he didn't have to lose very often. When I wrote Adams' obituary for the National Academy of Science, I noted the fact that he could do so many things well. He could be a leader in all ways.

My observing time was only a few nights of the month, controlled by the moon and clouds. Other observers had the use of the telescope at other times. During the light of the moon Adams and Joy and the spectroscopists used it; during the dark of the moon, Seares and I used it. At other times I worked at analyzing what we had seen. Another project was trying to discover variable stars in clusters, and occasionally Seares, who edited the Mount Wilson papers, would send a manuscript across the hall for me to edit. He knew about my newspaper writing and thought I could help on the science papers. I could, but only moderately well. Seares himself was an excellent editor.

My own research at Mount Wilson was concerned almost from the first with the distances of Cepheid variables. Some of the Cepheid variables are in the globular clusters, and that also interested me because the distances we could get with eclipsing binaries seemed to tie up with the distances from these Cepheid stars. Very early—in 1914—I did the paper on the pulsation theory of Cepheids which I have mentioned. I stayed with the Cepheids and clusters during those early years at Mount Wilson, until I crashed through on the distances and outlined the structure of the universe. I measured light curves and advanced the pulsation theory of Cepheids. I did a great deal of reading of the German contributions of R. Emden and A. Ritter that bore on vibrations in a mass of gas.

I was working especially on discovering new Cepheid variables. Solon I. Bailey at Harvard had found quite a number of them in clusters, and I found a lot more, including some of the important long-period Cepheids. They of course had the greater luminosities, and pretty soon I had some raw material that seemed to indicate great distances. I would say that almost from the beginning of my Mount Wilson days I was working on what the Cepheid variables could contribute to our understanding of what they are and how large they are.

The Shapley homestead in Barton County, Missouri, where Horace Shapley now lives. The one-room "Shapley School" *(right)* in which the boys received their early education was built on land donated by the Shapley family.

Laws Observatory at the University of Missouri, Columbia, as it looked when Shapley was an undergraduate.

Meeting of the Astronomical and Astrophysical Society of America, Pittsburgh, Pa., August 1912; the occasion on which Shapley (*extreme left*) delivered his first paper. E. C. Pickering, Shapley's predecessor as director of Harvard College Observatory, and at that time president of the Society, is in the center of the front row. Second to the right from Pickering is Annie J. Cannon and next right is Margaret Harwood, both of HCO. Dr. Adrian van Maanen (with bow tie), later a colleague of Shapley's at Mount Wilson Observatory, is behind Pickering, and Raymond S. Dugan of the Princeton Astronomy Department is to the right behind Miss Harwood.

Martha Betz Shapley with her daughter, Mildred, and her mother-in-law, Sarah Stowell Shapley, Pasadena, 1915.

Shapley and his two older children, Willis *(left)* and Mildred, riding an enormous seaweed, La Jolla, Calif., *c.* 1919.

George Ellery Hale, director of Mount Wilson Observatory, observing with the spectroheliograph in the Hale Solar Laboratory in Pasadena, at about the time Shapley began work at Mount Wilson. (Courtesy Mount Wilson and Palomar Observatories)

The 100-inch reflecting telescope at Mount Wilson, and *(below)*, in process of construction, the steel building and revolving dome that cover it, built in 1917. (From *The New Heavens* by George Ellery Hale, 1922)

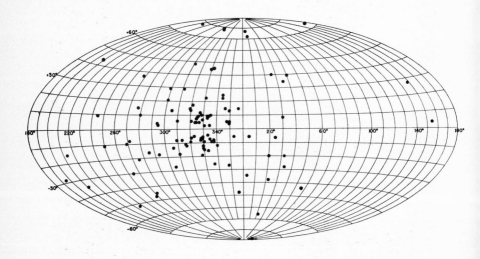

The location of globular clusters in the Milky Way galaxy led Shapley to his most important discovery: the Milky Way system is enormously larger than previously believed and the sun is near its periphery. Distribution of these clusters around the nucleus of the galaxy is shown in a hypothetical edge-on view *(left, top)* and is diagrammed in galactic coordinates *(left, bottom);* the 3 percent of the sky near the constellations Sagittarius and Scorpius *(below)* contains 39 of the 119 clusters recorded. (Left: top, from *The Dimensions and Structure of the Galaxy* by J. S. Plaskett, 1935; bottom, from *The Inner Metagalaxy* by Harlow Shapley, 1957. Below: Harvard College Observatory, courtesy Owen Gingerich)

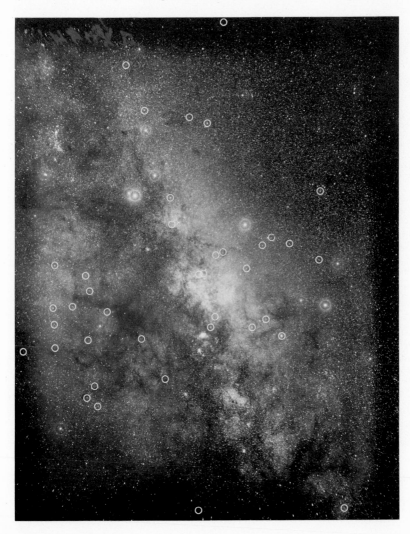

Shapley's opponent in the "great debate," Heber D. Curtis, at the eye-piece of the 24-inch reflecting telescope at Lick Observatory, Mount Hamilton, Calif.

Harvard College Observatory as it was when Shapley became director in 1921. The brick building *(rear left)* then housed the photographic plates for which a much larger building (known as "D") was added in 1932. The dome of the 15-inch telescope *(rear, right)* was flanked in front by the Library and at the back by the Observatory residence *(also shown in photograph at bottom).*

Annie J. Cannon *(left)* and Henrietta S. Leavitt, two great women astronomers on the HCO staff, at the entrance of the Observatory.

Solon I. Bailey, who was acting director of HCO between Pickering's death and Shapley's arrival. (Harvard College Observatory)

An Observatory tea on the lawn of the residence, 1924. At left staff members Donald H. Menzel, Willem J. Luyton, Leon Campbell; at far right Clyde Fisher of the American Museum of Natural History.

Ernest W. Brown, professor of mathematics at Yale University, with Shapley at the 18th annual meeting of the American Association of Variable Star Observers, HCO, 1929. (Clyde Fisher)

The Shapley family in 1928;
left to right: Alan, Willis,
Harlow, Lloyd, Carl, Martha,
and Mildred.

Shapley in the Observatory
office he inherited from Pickering, photographed about
1930 by HCO's second Ph.D.,
Frank Hogg. (Courtesy Helen
Sawyer Hogg)

Gaieties at the Observatory residence. *(Above)* A dramatic moment in the *Harvard Observatory Pinafore,* 1929; *left to right:* Peter Millman, Cecilia Payne, Henrietta Swope, Mildred Shapley, Helen Sawyer, Sylvia Mussells, Adelaide Ames, Leon Campbell. *(Below)* A masquerade celebrating a gift of money for the construction of Building "D," *c.* 1930.

Laying the cornerstone for the dome of the 61-inch telescope at the Oak Ridge Station, Harvard, Mass. At left is Sir Frank Dyson, Astronomer Royal.

An expedition to Plymouth, Mass., during the 1932 meeting of the International Astronomical Union; *left to right:* Sir Arthur S. Eddington, J. S. Plaskett, Walter S. Adams, Jan Oort, Henry Norris Russell, Harlow Shapley, W. K. Miller (of the Plymouth Chamber of Commerce), Sir Frank Dyson, Frederick Slocum, Bertil Lindblad.

Receiving the Rumford Medals awarded by the American Academy of Arts and Sciences for distinguished research in physics, 1933. Arthur E. Kennelly, chairman of the Rumford Committee, is presenting the medals; George H. Parker, president of the Academy, is at right. (Wide World photos)

At Chartres Cathedral, after the 1935 IAU meeting in Paris; *left to right:* Henry Norris Russell, Walter S. Adams, Shapley, Margaret Harwood, Mrs. Shapley, Mildred Shapley, Willis Shapley. (Mrs. Walter S. Adams; courtesy Margaret Harwood)

Albert Einstein at the Observatory residence on the occasion of his honorary degree from Harvard, 1935: *(right)* arriving, violin case in hand, for a musical evening; *(below)* with Donald H. Menzel *(left)*, Garrett Birkhoff, professor of mathematics at Harvard, and Carl Shapley.

The "foreign" group at HCO, 1939—astronomers, research assistants, and graduate students; *left to right: top row*—George Z. Dimitroff, Bulgarian; Cecilia H. Payne-Gaposchkin, English; Luigi Jacchia, Italian; *second row*—Donald MacRae, Canadian; Zdenek Kopal, Czech; Richard Prager, German; S. I. Gaposchkin, Russian; *third row*—Shirley Patterson, Canadian; Marie Paris Pishmish, Armenian-Turkish; Odon Godard, Belgian; *front row, seated*—Bart J. Bok, Dutch; Jaakko Tuominen, Finnish; Massaki Huruhata, Japanese; Luis Erro, Mexican.

At the famous rotating desk, here shown in the office in Building "D" to which it was moved about 1933. The central section of the desk also rotates independently; the bell underneath was used to summon staff members to the telephone. This photograph was taken about 1945.

The Copernican Quadricentennial, Carnegie Hall, New York City, 1943, at which Shapley presided. Albert Einstein is among the dignitaries on the stage *(at left)*.

A delegation from the Independent Voters Committee of the Arts and Sciences presenting Franklin D Roosevelt with a statement endorsing his re-election, October 1944; *left to right around Roosevelt:* Van Wyck Brooks, Hannah Dorner, Jo Davidson, Jan Kiepura, Joseph Cotten, Dorothy Gish, James Proctor, Shapley. (United Press International)

At the 220th anniversary of the Soviet (or Russian) Academy of Sciences, Moscow, 1945. Among the distinguished astronomers present are: *(front row, left to right)* British Astronomer Royal Sir Harold Spencer Jones, V. A. Vorontsov-Velyaminov, Shapley; *(second row)* K. A. Kulikov *(far left)*, B. V. Kukarkin *(third from right)*, P. P. Parenago *(far right)*; *(third row)* V. A. Ambartsumian *(far left)*, F. A. Orlov *(second from left)*; *(fourth row, far left)* K. T. Ogorodnikov.

On the way to Copenhagen, 1946, for a conference to restore the IAU, American representatives Shapley, Otto Struve, Joel Stebbins.

Leon Campbell, for many years Recorder for the American Association of Variable Star Observers, with the 8-inch telescope presented by Harvard in 1947 to Torun Observatory in Poland. (Robert E. Cox)

The Large Magellanic Cloud. A 411-minute exposure made in 1897 at the Harvard Southern Station at Arequipa, Peru. (Harvard College Observatory)

Boyden Station of HCO, Bloemfontein, South Africa, 1952. In the center is the dome of the 60-inch reflecting telescope. (*The Friend* newspaper, Bloemfontein; courtesy Harvard College Observatory)

Pope Pius XII greeting Dr. and Mrs. Shapley after the Pope's address to the 1952 meeting of the IAU assembly in Castel Gandolfo, Italy.

At the Moscow meeting of the IAU, 1958; *left to right:* F. J. M. Stratton, Gerard Kuiper, Ejnar Hertzsprung, Shapley. (Owen Gingerich)

Planning the documentary film made from *Of Stars and Men,*
c. 1960. (Jane Allner)

Then I got to the point where I had all the globular-cluster distances that this method and the usual trigonometric methods could give me.

I plotted the clusters and looked at what I had. I found that globular clusters are mostly in the southern Milky Way and that some are bright and some faint. Those that contain Cepheid variables could be compared with those that do not. Finally I hit upon using the period-luminosity relation that had been foreshadowed by Miss Henrietta Leavitt at Harvard in a paper published in 1912. Her paper dealt with only twenty-five stars and did not deal with their distances at all. So I went after the distances, and that was helped by Ejnar Hertzsprung's work.

Besides the resident staff at Mount Wilson, there were visitors who used the observatory, and in the early days J. C. Kapteyn was the most persistent of these. He was of the older school, but one of the most famous European astronomers. He came in July of the year that I came and stayed on the mountain most of the time. The cottage on Mount Wilson is still called the Kapteyn cottage.

I took Kapteyn my first measures of the distance of globular clusters and said, "The method that I've been telling you about—the method of getting the distances of objects with these variable stars in Messier 3—gives this sort of result. I'd like to have you see it." He looked and suggested that I check my observations again. In other words, he would not accept the result. But he was kind about it, because I was a nice young man and he was a nice old man.

There was no question about my having hit the jackpot, but Kapteyn was attacking the distance problem in a very different way, as a part of proper-motion studies. He did not want to give up his own methods, which were good but very rough. It was eight years after I announced my distance to the Milky Way center before Kapteyn halfway accepted it.

Among the other visitors was Robert Williams Wood, the physicist from Johns Hopkins, whom I had met at Princeton when I was first there. The famous Albert Michelson was there for some time measuring the velocity of light between two mountain tops.

Somewhat later Russell began coming out as an associate. In fact, it was pointed out that if I would take the Harvard job, it would release funds and they could get Russell full time. That was rather an interesting situation. But they got him to come anyway for short periods. He was the judge of astronomy for all of us, and he was always very useful when he came around. He could discuss any astronomical topic, with two or three exceptions. He did not work on the structure of the Milky Way, even in later years when Bart Bok was deep in it—he just didn't turn his mind that way. And he would not work on long-period variable stars in spite of the growing interest in them by amateur observers. He was baffled that Miss Cannon and I and some others knew the names and numbers of scores of them; he did not like to have us go past him. But as far as I remember he knew everything else—he was the universal judge of all problems.

One of the solar astronomers on the staff, Seth B. Nicholson, occasionally came around to use the 60-inch telescope on my nights. He was interested in Jupiter. Nobody else was, but Nicholson was a Jupiter type of astronomer, who had found a new Jovian satellite in 1914. Together we found an object which we thought was another new moon of Jupiter. Now one rule of astronomy is that if you find a new asteroid or a comet or some similar object, you go on and make a study of it. We had found what we called "a doggoned asteroid or something," and we had to get the orbit. It was the only orbit of that kind I ever computed. Nicholson and I labored heavily, got an orbit, and published it in 1916. The thing turned out to be an asteroid, not a satellite of Jupiter.

It is also one of the rules to name such a trivial object, because asteroids must have names or numbers. We flipped a penny to see who would get a chance to name the asteroid, and I won the toss. My first thought was to name it for my wife, buying some credit at home. But Martha was already in the sky as the name of another of the hundreds of asteroids. Then I thought about my mother-in-law, whose name is Louise. But Louise also was in the sky. "Very well, we shall wait." Sure enough, the oncoming infant was female, and the asteroid was promptly named Mildred.

Twice in those days we went to Hale's house—once was when W. W. Campbell of the Lick Observatory came down during the First World War. Campbell had a son in the war and was really passionate about killing Germans, as many people were then. St. John was pretty rough on the Germans, and Adams was, but Hale was not. He took it quietly. The younger ones, like Van Maanen and Paul W. Merrill and myself, were pretty well suspect because we thought there might be another side to some issues. That was before we actually got into war.

Later a little war work was done by Arthur King and Harold D. Babcock—making gratings and so forth—but very little. Hale asked me personally not to enlist, as I was about to do in spite of having two or three kids and exemptions. Hale said, "You want to be available for optical work that may come to Washington." That was working with the National Research Council, making better cameras and that kind of thing. Adams later okayed my enlisting, and I was in the process of joining the coast artillery when the Kaiser said "Uncle."

George W. Ritchey made optics for the government, but he ran into difficulty with Adams for making things on the side. I liked Ritchey pretty well, but I like everybody I can think of. I knew him in Paris later, when he set up shop in the Paris observatory. I felt sorry for him because he was so difficult. Hale tolerated him, but some of the others did not. Ritchey was opposed to completing the 100-inch telescope, which made more difficulty.

I knew about the plans for the 100-inch from the start, and Pease and I were the first users. It was a long time after our preliminary use before the giant was in really good shape; then it became a very powerful tool. The first night the 100-inch was used officially was November 1, 1917. Hale came back from Washington for the occasion, and Alfred Noyes, the poet, was there too, writing his bad poetry! I write this exactly fifty years later—1917-1967. I was not present at this "dedication."

Adrian van Maanen came to Mount Wilson within two or three years after I did. He at once became a friend of Mr. Hale. Van Maanen was aggressive and he was sociable. He could go to a dinner and soon have the whole table laughing. He was a social success. People liked him—until he became a sort of playboy.

Van Maanen's job at Mount Wilson was measuring galaxies, and stellar parallaxes, and the sun's magnetic field by way of the Zeeman effect. He worked for Hale and was soon getting the rotation of galaxies. It looks now as though he got the answers he wanted, or that seemed to be best. I don't know that he ever corrected himself, but others have corrected him. He was a charming person, a bachelor; he and I were pals of a sort—I don't know why, because I wasn't "society" and he was. I suppose we got together because he was rather an alert-minded person and I liked his nonsense. Hubble disliked Van Maanen from the time he himself arrived on Mount Wilson; he scorned him. Hubble just didn't like people. He didn't associate with them, didn't care to work with them. I remember once somebody referred a paper of mine to Hubble for him to pass judgment on. It was a good paper; it was correct; I mean I knew what I was talking about at that time. It was written for some journal like *Scientific American.* Hubble just wrote across it, "Of no consequence." The editors, who told me about it, thought it was the funniest thing, because the words, "Shapley—of no consequence," got set in type.

Hubble and I did not visit very much. He was a Rhodes scholar, and he didn't live it down. He spoke with a thick Oxford accent. He was born in Missouri not far from where I was born and probably knew the Missourian tongue. But he spoke "Oxford." He would use such phrases as "to come a cropper." The ladies he associated with enjoyed that Oxford touch very much. "Bah Jove!" he would say, and other such expressions. He was quite picturesque.

People have sometimes wondered why I did not work on galaxies when I had the tools all ready and the methods worked out on clusters. The work that Hubble did on galaxies was very largely using my methods, even to using the five brightest stars as a criterion of distance. He never acknowledged my priority, but there are people like that. Hubble had done his doctoral thesis at Yerkes on the clusters of "nebulae." It was logical that, when he came to Mount Wilson after the First World War, he would go on with galaxies. Seares pointed out that Hubble could then do for spiral galaxies what I had been doing for clusters. Hubble went on and made himself very famous, and properly so. He was an excellent observer, better than I. In my book *Galaxies* (1943; 1961) his picture appears, as our leading student of galaxies.

The research at Mount Wilson was organized in specific assignments. Each of us worked on our assigned themes, without much overlapping. Photometry was Seares's field. Adams and Joy were spectroscopists. A. Kohlschütter, who went to Germany to fight in the First World War, with Adams did a fine job using the spectra of the stars as a criterion of distance. It got a big hand at the time, but the field has now been so extended that the work of Adams and Kohlschütter is hardly remembered.

We kept away from one another's fields remarkably well; it was rather surprising that we did. I kept up with other fields of science by reading the literature very fully. Nicholson was also pretty good with the literature, but in general we were all so busy with our observations that we did not have a chance for speculation. The instruments just had to be used because they were the best in the world. We never let a good clear night go by without feeling bad about it. In those days we did no teaching, no lecturing. Our goal was to do things we had not done before, to be leaders in scientific research, and to live up to Hale's dream of Mount Wilson as a research institution.

I never especially regretted not going on with galaxies at

Mount Wilson. But that was the situation when Heckmann of Hamburg wrote an article describing my work, in which he said, "The thing that bothers us and that we don't understand is why Shapley just quit." I didn't quit. I worked like the dickens. But I was using the tools that appropriately were permitted me.

After the first paper on the pulsation hypothesis, I went on for three or four years following it through and getting the distances of the clusters and their arrangements in space. My first paper on this was published in about 1917, and then I did a number of papers backing it up or extending it. This was the series of papers called "Studies Based on the Colors and Magnitudes in Stellar Clusters."

Some of my series of papers on globular clusters published in 1917 and 1918 were rather revolutionary because the findings opened up a part of the universe that had not been known before. They showed a way to measure enormous distances and also revealed the position of the clusters in the universe. When we finally got the full picture of globular-cluster distribution, we had about a hundred clusters and estimates of their distances. Some of my distances were wrong, but a lot of them were right. The cluster of clusters is in one part of the sky, in the region of Sagittarius—"the home of the globular clusters," it has been called. Another part of the sky is more or less empty of globular clusters. The results could not be disproved except by claiming that the measurements were wrong or crooked. So they were accepted, except by the cautious people who did not want changes.

The result was what might be called a three-dimensional picture of our galaxy—our own part of the universe. In it the solar system is off center and consequently man is too, which is a rather nice idea because it means that man is not such a big chicken. He is incidental—my favorite term is "peripheral." He is on the perimeter of this operation. And he cannot very well be put anywhere else, especially since there are a lot of wheel-shaped galaxies like this one of ours. So it looked as though we had support from the heavens themselves for the idea that the center is in Sagittarius.

After I saw that mankind was peripheral, it occurred to me that this had philosophical implications, but I did not follow up the idea. I just noticed it. Then later I found it one of the most important thoughts I have ever had: finding the peripheral position of the solar system had a very definite bearing on how the universe was put together. If man had been found in the center, it would look sort of natural. We could say, "Naturally we are in the center because we are God's children." But here was an indication that we were perhaps incidental. We did not amount to so much. About that time, with some help from Seares and others, I came to the conclusion that there must be a hundred thousand million stars in this one galaxy of ours.

That was a shocker—a rearrangement of man in the sidereal universe. First there had been the geocentric universe, then the heliocentric, then the galactocentric. In the geocentric theory the earth was the center. Then the Copernican view was accepted, the sun being the center. (It is not quite as simple as that, of course, but that about expresses it.) Then here comes the overthrow of the Copernican theory. In one of my books, *The View from a Distant Star* (1963), the first chapter is called "Two Moments of Discovery." Finding the center was one of those moments.

Another article of mine, which has been published many

times, in many places, including my book *Of Stars and Men* (1958), is called "The Fourth Adjustment." Man has adjusted himself to one after another of these centers; a fourth adjustment is required when the factor of life is brought into the picture.

I like to point out that even if only one star in a billion has planets that could have biological metabolism operating, there are so many stars that there would still be a hundred thousand million that have or have had life. Three things make a fourth adjustment necessary. One is the tremendous number of stars in the universe—more than 10^{20} (1 with 20 zeros after it). The second is the new knowledge of how planetary systems can be formed—namely, from a shrinking, twirling mass of gas. The third is the knowledge that life is an automatic and natural phenomenon in cosmic evolution. We see that there is no trick in the origin of life. There was a time when the appearance of life was explained by Genesis and the supernatural. But the supernatural is no longer needed in accounting for the origin and development of life. I think that is a rather impressive conclusion.

I have mentioned that the cautious were skeptical about my work on globular clusters. One of the most skeptical was Heber D. Curtis of Lick Observatory, who was a very conservative person. He thought—and said: "You are all wrong. This is a wild business." Somebody—perhaps Seares—suggested that we argue it out in public and that led to what later became known as "The Great Debate." But before I get to that, I want to go off on a tangent, which also belongs in part to the Mount Wilson period.

Chapter Five

FORMICID EPISODES

Not all my observing on the mountain was done with a telescope—I had another interest. A year or so after I came to Mount Wilson I had climbed down into the canyon below the engineering building to collect different kinds of shrubs. To return was a hard climb and I rested lazily when I got to the top. While resting I saw a stream of ants running along a concrete wall—some were going one way and some another. They ran from some shrubbery up one side of the building that we called "the shop" and down the other side, along the wall. I had not been interested scientifically in ants up to that time, but I noticed that when the ants went into the shade of the manzanita bushes, they slowed down—just as I would have done. It was cool and nice, and I supposed that they slowed down for comfort. I began to wonder about this, however, and soon I got a thermometer and a barometer and a hydrometer and all those "ometers," and a stop watch. I set up a sort of observing station while resting and getting ready for another night's tussle with the globular clusters. With a flashlight I followed those ants in the dark, and I found it great fun to watch them.

Whether they were carrying loads or not, they went at about the same speed. I set up several "speed traps" for them. To run thirty centimeters took them about so many seconds. But not at midday. In the noontime heat the ants ran faster. So I discovered the thermokinetics of ants—the higher the temperature, the faster they run. (The same is true of snakes and lizards.) They are not influenced by pressure or moisture, or by anything except air temperature. By observing half a dozen ants through my speed trap, I could tell the temperature to within one degree. That is one way to get the temperature. Another method is to read your thermometer.

These ants were of a particular species—*Liometopum apiculatum*, the trail runners. They are medium-sized brownish-black ants, and there were hundreds of them in the nest. They really make trails. They wear a path in the dust along the concrete wall—not actually in the concrete; they are not that good.

When I went back to Mount Wilson thirty years later, they were still running that same trail along the same concrete wall, in spite of the fact that the assistant engineer goes along with a blow torch occasionally and decimates them. I do not know why he does. We did not often speak to each other after that genocide.

I observed these ants first on the mountain and later in Pasadena. Then I went on to other species. I used to go down to West Fork with Milton Humason, who was at that time the caretaker on the mountain, and while he fished I would go looking for ants. I saw *Polyergus*—the famous slavemakers. I wanted to find *Tapinoma sessile,* a well-known low-slung trail runner that does not run very fast. I just didn't see him (I should say "her") anywhere. So I wrote to William Morton Wheeler at Harvard, who was the top ant man of the planet, and complained: "You say that we should find *Tapinoma sessile* in this part of California. I have looked and I do not find it. I wonder if I have it wrongly identified." He wrote back: "Just be patient; they're there." And, sure enough, they were there. I could not find them, but they found me. Thousands of them crawled through our Pasadena basement, a stream of *Tapinoma sessile*. They went through the den and into the kitchen sink where they got moisture. I had my experiment running right there in front of me. It involved my wife; she does not hold with ants quite as much as I do. I already had the temperature-speed ratio for some ants all the way down to the edge of a snow bank, where they travel very slowly at about 35 degrees Fahrenheit, and all the way up to about 100 degrees, when they travel rapidly, but I wanted to get the speed as the ants got hotter and hotter. When the temperature reached about 100 degrees there were no more volunteers running, and I could not get any more points on my curve. But I noticed that one of the streams of *Tapinoma sessile* ran through my den in going to and from the kitchen sink. That gave me a hunch, so I stripped completely, turned up the furnace, and got the temperature in the den up to about 103 degrees. Some of the ants fell from the wall—they could not take it. Something happens when the temperature gets to 100 degrees. Maybe the metabolism goes sour. Maybe the joints stiffen. But I got the desired readings for my temperature-speed curves.

Mount Wilson provided me with ideal conditions. It gave me the leisure to make observations both day and night and provided in my environment a temperature range of about 70 degrees. I wrote several small articles on ants, which were published; then I realized that I was in danger of spoiling a harmless hobby.

My colleagues knew about my ant-running, of course. Some thought, Shapley's funny. Others were interested scientifically, especially Seth Nicholson. But I kept it mostly to myself. I don't know what Hale would have thought, but probably he would have approved. Seares was amused, though he was a cool fellow. When I went into his publication office with my article "On the Thermokinetics of Dolichoderine Ants," he pushed it away. He would not read my papers on ants. He may have thought I was doing a stunt. In a way I was, but it was fun. I was and am excited about ants. They taught me things.

I have gone on looking at queer ants and ant sociology all around the world. I have played with the Argentine menace and with *Solenopsis,* the well-named fire ant. *Atta* must also be mentioned—the peak of ant civilization. I saw its agricultural operations. I can hold forth for hours with ant stories—"formicid episodes" I call them.

I used *Liometopum apiculatum* when I gave the Commencement address at the University of Pennsylvania. The title was "On Running in Trails." That is what graduates are likely to do unless they take care—they will run in trails, do just what their ancestors did, never venture out to the side; they will run in trails just like my Dolichoderine ants.

I have given lectures at agricultural schools and elsewhere on social insects—not that I know much about them, but other people seem to know much less. The ants that you see around are infertile females; only the queen and the males carry on the sex business. When you see ants running around and bringing in food or laying a scent trail, these activities are just part of their economy and psyche. They're pretty decent to their people at home.

I still try to read almost everything written on ants. I think I know the first and second names—the genus and species—of about 30 kinds of ants. But there are more than 10,000 kinds.

One ant episode happened in Egypt. I picked up some

pygmy ants off a camel's dunghill at the base of an Egyptian pyramid. I had left my vial at home, so I could not pickle them in the proper way. With me, watching in wonderment, was the distinguished biophysicist Detlev Bronk. He saw that I was distressed because I had no vodka with me—in fact, nothing to pickle ants in. He lent me his watch; we unscrewed the crystal, put one of the ants inside, and shut it up. Thus I had with me the beginning of a menagerie. The ant crawled over to five minutes of eleven and perished. Eventually that ant was lost at sea.

The worst formicid trouble I had in Africa was when I picked up some ants on the shore of Lake Victoria, exactly on the Equator. For an astronomer that is a sentimental sort of place. You can see the North Pole star, and at the same time see the stars at the South Pole, because refraction slightly lifts the Poles. I looked forward to that moment, but it rained steadily the whole time we were in the vicinity, so I did not get any astronomical satisfaction out of that formicid adventure.

I did, however, later gather some near-equatorial ants. Again I had no vial with me; this time I pickled them in my tobacco pouch. I had a fairly good grade of tobacco, and I put the ants in with the nicotine, where they promptly smothered. A little later, when I was flying to South Africa to investigate Harvard's southern observatory, I got into a card game with some officers of the British Navy. Most of them were pretty clever, but one of them (my partner) was stupid enough to lean over to see some elephants—he was hunting elephants by airplane from a mile or so above Mozambique. In Dar es Salaam they had told us, "You can see them in flocks!" I did not see them. He did not see them either, but he displayed his cards to our opposition and we got badly stuck. It annoyed me to have a good bridge game spoiled by this officer's foolish ambition. So I hauled out my jimmy briar and calmed my nervous anger with a solacing pipe. Later I found that my ants had all been smoked away! It was sad because I had carried them so far.

There were other formicid affairs that were amusing. One of them was at the end of the Second World War when sixteen Americans got on a flight bound for Moscow. The Russians gave us a big farewell feast (on lend-lease supplies, I suppose). There were about eleven hundred present to help celebrate the winning of the war. The "government," Stalin, and all the big shots were present. The Red Chorus was there, and the ballerinas. I sat there happily, with the rest of the Americans. You can get happy after a while, just seeing so many people drinking vodka.

And do you know what happened? A wobbly ant crawled off the bowl of bananas they had put in front of me. It fell on the table and started briskly for Joe Stalin, one hundred yards away. I said, "That won't do" and pulled out my vial. It had in it some stuff from a Boston drugstore that was called alcohol. I tried to interest the colonel opposite me—I suppose he was a colonel, anyway he was some sort of officer in the Russian Army. We didn't know each other's languages, but we giggled. We were having a good time. Then another ant came unsteadily along. "When they wake up in the Soviet heaven," I argued, "they would certainly want ambrosia and nectar." I poured out the "alcohol" onto a bun and filled up my little vial with vodka. Then I needed ambrosia so that the ants would have a proper balanced diet when they got to heaven. I got two fish eggs from a bowl of caviar. Then I showed the vial around the table. The colonel was very happy about it too. I sealed the vial and took it home—the two ants with the two fish eggs.

I showed them to the various and sundry who came to my office—Shapley's Kremlin ants became rather notorious. Then I changed my office, alas, and that little vial of ants disappeared. I looked for it a good deal and eventually found a vial properly labeled as to place and time but with only one ant in it. This is one of the mysteries in my life. What could have happened? Did it mean that one of the Red-chasers from the House Un-American Activities Committee had caught up with me and was trying to confuse me or something? The caviar had disappeared also, but anything might disappear in 100-volt vodka.

The ant could not have disappeared coming through customs because I carry my valuables in my coat pocket close to my heart. One ant could not have eaten the other, because they were the same size and make, and anyway ants do not eat one another. It is not ethical.

I took the vial home to my wife. I said, "Look what has happened. I did have two ants in the vial. It is still sealed, and there it is: one ant! I can't understand what happened to the other ant. I can explain the galaxy somewhat, but this is quite beyond me."

Whereupon my wife said, "I have a hypothesis if you want one to explain that situation of two ants and then one."

"Well, what is it?" (I shouldn't stick my neck out like that.)

"Well, my hypothesis is that people who go to vodka parties can't count very well."

I can go on and on about ants; it is rather amusing to find an ancient civilization such as ants have had for fifty million years, whereas primates have been around for only a few hundred thousand years. Any entomologist will tell you that the insects are far beyond us in social development.

Chapter Six

THE GREAT DEBATE

During the Mount Wilson years my series of papers on "Colors and Magnitudes in Stellar Clusters," continued to develop. As I mentioned earlier, Heber D. Curtis at the Lick Observatory, who was one of the best observers and talkers about the universe, was skeptical concerning the Mount Wilson work. He started out as a classicist, which appealed to me but didn't help much when he began talking about where the globular clusters are. This was not jealousy on his part; he was just doubtful as to whether the spirals were going down the right groove. His skepticism included doubt about Van Maanen's work to some extent, and especially about mine on clusters which had led rather naturally and cleanly to my new method of measuring big distances and therefore to my new views on the size of the universe and how it is put together. If one looks at the papers Curtis wrote at the time, one wonders how he got that way, because the evidence is so much against his conservative conclusion.

At the same time, he was right on some points, especially on where the spiral galaxies fit into the sidereal scheme. A paper or two of mine, and maybe two of his, were quite antagonistic. He had his strong views, and I published my data on the arrangement of stars in the universe. I think Seares believed that what I was doing was right, and he may have taken it up with Hale who was then managing National Academy of Sciences affairs. It was natural enough for a person with a quick mind like Hale's to say, "Well, let's fight it out.

Let's see what it is all about. This is sensational if Shapley is right."

I think Hale wanted to have his colleagues help him make up his mind. He really was deeply interested in these things, although the sun was his major concern.

Pretty soon an invitation came by way of Hale for Curtis and me to fight it out in public at the annual meeting of the National Academy of Sciences in Washington, on April 26, 1920. I accepted, of course; I had no choice. Hale gave me a check for $250 to pay for the trip. Perhaps he felt a little guilty at having got me into it. I would have gone anyway; we had already resigned ourselves to poverty.

Hale was naturally generous. Rather early in my time at Mount Wilson, he called me into his office and said, "You know everybody around here and know them well. Would you keep your eyes open for people who are in need? Perhaps I could help a little, but quietly, without their knowing it?"

I don't know whether Milton Humason yet knows that the publication of one of his first papers was paid for by a secret gift from Hale. I think that was the only case I dug up. Humason had started his career on Mount Wilson as caretaker. Seth Nicholson and I taught him arithmetic and calculus. We encouraged him because he had faith and stability. To be sure, he thought he could be a water diviner and find water on the mountain top. We had to shake that out of him.

At first Hale was opposed to appointing Humason to the staff because he thought Humason did not have the training; then later Hale said, "I was wrong." Humason became one of the best observers we ever had, and the credit goes mostly to Nicholson for teaching him. I may have excited him somewhat and said, "Hooray, go to it," but I was too selfish to help him much. Nicholson would sit down and tell him what cosines are. Humason finally got an honorary doctor's degree from Lund, Sweden. That was lovely. That was something that we couldn't do then in this country—give an honorary degree to a man who did not finish high school. But the Swedes could and did.

To get back to the "debate," I think most of the people at Mount Wilson accepted what I was saying. After all, Seares would edit paper after paper that kept flowing along every month or so, and he never stopped the flow.

Before we went to Washington, Curtis and I had talked together a bit, but not very much. I went to the Lick Observatory on Mount Hamilton to see him. I don't think he came to Mount Wilson. Anyway, he was pretty positive in what he said, and I felt that my observations were positive in what they said.

According to an account by the astronomer Otto Struve, statements were prepared by both of us and exchanged before the meeting, but that is not my recollection. Perhaps he was thinking of the exchange of papers after the meeting prior to publication. Curtis and I knew each other's views, so we would not have needed to exchange papers.

Curtis and I both went to Washington, by train of course —Southern Pacific—and we found ourselves on the same train. When Curtis made his charming presentation to the Academy, he said, "Although we came on the same train and talked about this and that" (I think I collected some ants wherever the train stopped long enough) "there is no collusion. We haven't discussed this matter. We haven't argued it. So it's fresh." In fact, when the train broke down in Alabama, we walked back and forth and talked about flowers and classical subjects. It was quite pleasant. But we deliberately kept away from the controversial subject—the Great Debate.

On the evening of the debate there was a banquet. Hale sent me a ticket, and I sat at a table with some noted people. One was Raymond Pearl of Johns Hopkins, the student of alcohol effects. Another was W. J. V. Osterhout of the Harvard department of botany. We talked and gossiped. Then came the speech making. It was just horrible. The Academy gives various prizes and hands out medals of one kind and another. On this occasion it was honoring the Prince of Monaco for oceanography, and several others. One I particularly remember was some noble operator from a government bureau who had worked successfully on hookworm control. That was his specialty, his life.

But none of these people were exciting as speakers. They did not know how to make a talk. One would talk for a long while about "Johnson the Scientist," "Johnson as Operator," "Johnson the Man"—those were the kinds of phrases they used. And then another would get up and do much the same. I groaned.

Over at the end of the head table there was a visitor from Europe named Albert Einstein. He was sitting there with a beaming face that reflected his wonderful personality. Alongside him, I believe, was the secretary from the Netherlands embassy who was there on behalf of the physicist Pieter Zeeman to receive a prize, a medal, or something of that kind. And here all these non-speakers droned on and on. To me it was embarrassing, to others also, but Einstein, smiling, leaned over to the Dutchman and whispered something. The Dutchman turned away quickly to hide his big smile or possibly guffaw. "What did Einstein say?" we asked the Dutchman afterward. "He said, 'I have just got a new theory of Eternity.' "

As for the actual "debate," I must point out that I had forgotten about the whole thing long ago, and nobody had mentioned it to me for many years. Then, beginning about eight or ten years ago, it was talked about again. To have it come up suddenly as an issue, and as something historic, was a surprise, for at the time I had just taken it for granted. Curtis was right partly, and I was right partly. Then this Great Debate was featured as parts of two chapters of *Astronomy of the 20th Century* (1962) by Otto Struve and Velta Zebergs and is described in any number of other publications. I don't know who first dug it up or when, and I'm also puzzled as to why. I don't think the word "debate" was used at the time (in 1920). Actually it was a sort of symposium, a paper by Curtis and a paper by me, and a rebuttal apiece. Now I would know how to dodge things a little better. Curtis did a moderately good job. Some of his science was wrong, but his delivery was all right. As I have said, he was a classicist.

There were two or three hundred people present; the Academy was not as big as it is now. Not many astronomers were there. Very few of them went to the Academy meetings in those days; Hale had not yet got them inspired to attend.

Anyway, it was a pleasant meeting, and our subject matter was the scale of the universe. That was what I was prepared to talk about and did talk about, and I think I won the "debate" from the standpoint of the assigned subject matter. I was right and Curtis was wrong on the main point—the scale, the size. It is a big universe, and he viewed it as a small one. From the beginning Curtis picked on another matter: are the spiral galaxies inside our system or outside? He said that they are outside systems. I said, "I don't know what they are, but according to certain evidences they are not outside."

But that was not the assigned subject. Curtis, having set

up this straw man, won on that. I was wrong because I was banking on Van Maanen's measures of large proper motions in spirals. If you have large proper motions you are dealing with things near at hand. I consider this as a blunder of mine because I faithfully went along with my friend Van Maanen and *he* was wrong on the proper motions of galaxies—that is, their cross motions. Although Curtis and Hubble and some others discredited Van Maanen's measures and questioned his conclusions, I stood by Van Maanen. I was wrong, not so much in any statement that I made, but in the inference that the spirals must be inside and not outside our system.

So it was a double win and a double loss. In a sense we were talking about two different things. The most nearly correct description of the affair, which has been much misrepresented, is by Struve and Zebergs. They have it practically the way I have told it here, but a good many others have not got it straight. They wonder why Shapley made this blunder. The reason he made it was that Van Maanen was his friend and he believed in friends!

As I remember it, I read my paper and Curtis presented his paper, probably not reading much because he was an articulate person and was not scared. Then I replied, and then he replied. My reply was on the basis of what he had said and why it was wrong. And he came to his famous phrase: "There are some observations that are not worth a damn, and others that are not worth a damn. In my opinion, two damns are no better than one damn." He got his laugh.

Later I too recognized that Van Maanen's measurements were wrong. Knut Lundmark came over from Sweden to go through the measuring of the rotations of the galaxies, and he could not verify Van Maanen's figures. But he was a gentleman; he did not want to criticize them publicly. When I found it was a false trail I switched immediately to the truth; I have been complimented more than once on that since. Curtis also yielded pretty soon on the scale of the universe.

Our papers were published by the National Research Council, which was probably the hand of Hale again. The debate was called the William Ellery Hale Lecture because the money came out of a fund for such things which Hale set up in memory of his father. When the papers finally appeared, they were somewhat different from the actual speeches. There was some yielding on both sides.

The strongest comment I can make about the affair now is how little I remember about it, although it was important in my career. At the time the Harvard job was hovering, and things went on developing. There was no lack of prestige for everybody.

A by-product of the trip to Washington that seems to me more important than the so-called debate was that I was examined by George Russell Agassiz and Theodore Lyman to see if I would be a decent character to be the director of the Harvard College Observatory. They took me for an automobile ride to wherever I was going. They were big shots from Harvard making "the lookover." Another big shot who was not so big, Professor J. C. Duncan of Wellesley College, was asked to examine the female of the family to see if she would fit into the Harvard community. Harvard took pains about that kind of thing. Duncan interviewed her and made a report, and she was approved.

I was expecting the interview because they had written me that they were coming to Washington and wanted to see me. E. C. Pickering, who had been the director of the observatory for about forty years, had died in 1919; naturally appointing a new director for such a big observatory is not done in a minute. The day I heard that Pickering had died, on my way home for lunch I stopped at the corner of two streets—I could name them now—and pondered on whether I should give up a research career. "Should I, or should I not? Should I curb my ambition?" Finally I said to myself, "All right. I'll take a shot at it." It was a deliberate choice.

After the interviews in Washington I went on to Harvard and got acquainted. I saw Joel Metcalfe who was on the visiting committee. I indirectly let the people there know that I would not be averse to being considered for the directorship.

When I asked Russell what he thought about it, he said, "Oh, no, no, you wouldn't want to do that. You couldn't do that." Russell was very much disturbed that I was considering it seriously. So was William Pickering, who wrote a letter, which somebody sent to me, saying, "I didn't think Shapley would be so foolish as to give up his astronomical career just to be director of that observatory." That was the view some friends took, and it annoyed me so much that I have since taken pains to do scientific work in spite of being the director of the Harvard Observatory. In fact, I think I did as much scientific work as anybody for the twenty years after I went to Harvard.

Russell himself had been offered the directorship indirectly, but no one expected him to accept. They knew he wanted to stay at Princeton, and also his health was not too good. After he had written me that I should not take it, he changed his mind and decided I should by all means accept.

The real reason I got the job—this isn't wholly true, but

I'll tell it as if it were—was this. Those ants I have talked about—there is a flow of energy this way and that way—well, both stars and ants are energetic operators, so I have a sort of excuse to play around with ants. But I had to get some of my little crawlers identified. In California that was not easy. Ant students are scarce. I bottled a sample of ants and set up an exchange with William Morton Wheeler, philosopher, biologist, and myrmecologist, who had fiddled around with ants for half a century and had written a book on them. Wheeler heard that Harvard was looking for an astronomer whom they could appoint as observatory director. He went to see A. Lawrence Lowell, the president of Harvard, and said, "I don't know how this person is in astronomy. I am not pretending to know whether his astronomy is any good. But he is very good in myrmecology. I think you ought to hire him."

Another reason I was considered was that thanks to some very skillful boys on the football team, Harvard won the Eastern title in 1920. That made the alumni in the West very excited. They were being solicited for gifts to Harvard. The amount was rather large for those days, though not for today. They had suggested that the football team be sent out West as a part of the public relations. The faculty said, "No," whereupon the Corporation said "Yes," and sent the team out. It annoyed some of the faculty, but they were told, "We have to raise money and one of the ways to raise money is to play against Oregon." With the team they sent a man who was called the Provost. He traveled with the football team, but his mission was to look at Shapley. I was sent some free tickets, and Mrs. Shapley and I watched the game in the Rose Bowl in Pasadena. Now came the "gamble." As luck would have it, the Harvard team won. Nobody expected them to win because they were gentlemen, not football brutes, but they did—the score was 7 to 6. So back East they decided they would take a gamble also on me.

I don't think Harvard ever sent another team to the West Coast. Afterward George Russell Agassiz used to say that the way they select a man to be director of the observatory is first to check with the captain of the football team. So what with Wheeler, the football captain, the score, and my wife, I got the job!

Agassiz, incidentally, became a personal friend and was a very important factor in the Harvard Observatory over the forty years I was there. He was a member of the famous Agassiz family, the son of Alexander Agassiz and the grandson of Louis, and a Harvard alumnus of weight and also of cash. He paid a good many bills for the Observatory—not the big ones because he gave his big money to the Museum of Comparative Zoology. Once when there were certain unpleasant operations at the Museum he came to me and said, "How can we change my will?" I said, "You'll feel better about it in a few days," which he did. Agassiz supported me more than the astronomers did. He knew enough astronomy. He even wrote a book about Mars; he believed, along with his good friend Percival Lowell, that there were canals on Mars. He said to me—it sounded as though Hale were speaking—"Shapley, don't do research that other people want you to do. Do what you want to do." It turned out that I did both.

Negotiations were completed sometime in 1920, and I went to Harvard in April 1921. I went with the title of "observer." They had never had such a title before, but they didn't quite want to call me "director." But the understanding was fairly clear, because the aforementioned Mr. Hale had written a letter to Lowell that contained a statement something like this: "If Dr. Shapley is the able man that we think he is, you don't want to offer him a subservient position, but the directorship of the observatory." Hale said that, and one of Lowell's assistants told me that it turned the trick. Lowell had complete faith in Hale, and Hale wrote such skillful letters.

So I went with some understanding that I was chosen for the real job, but for technical reasons they held out the title for a few months. It was supposed to be for a year, but some reorganization was urgent, and they gave me the title in six months.

In my decision to take the job, I think a feeling of responsibility was a leading consideration. Here was an observatory that was a bit run down and didn't have a very brilliant staff. It had the famous Annie Cannon, and the careful E. S. King, who was a photometrist of sorts, and Bailey, but nobody like the people who were at Mount Wilson at that time. Therefore here was a chance to build it up. In his last years Pickering just carried on the routine, and the place was essentially vacant for about two years after his death before I took over.

After I came in, the Observatory started to grow, almost at once. George Russell Agassiz helped, and I raised money elsewhere when it was necessary. For a good many years I think the Harvard College Observatory was tops. It is a pretty good place now, but we have tough competition from our own products!

I really didn't have any serious misgivings about leaving Mount Wilson after my seven years there. I felt that I was ready to leave, and my pals, like Nicholson and Merrill, felt that I had finally arrived. I'd been making a lot of noise and doing things; they expected me to make good. And I did, partly. I could of course do better now if I had a chance to do it over.

Chapter Seven

HARVARD COLLEGE
OBSERVATORY

It was in April of 1921 that I went on to Harvard. Mrs. Shapley and the three children—Mildred, Willis, and Alan—stayed in Kansas City while I got the big house prepared. After a few weeks they followed me. There were problems about the children's music and their schooling, so Mrs. Shapley was kept pretty busy that spring—and has been ever since. Lloyd and Carl were born later, in Cambridge.

I mentioned that both Mrs. Shapley and I were investigated rather thoroughly to see whether we were at a proper social level for Harvard. When we got there, we were treated nicely. I was made a member of a number of the good dining clubs. Although I did not have anything to do with undergraduate students, I did meet with faculty a great deal. There were a number of growth operations in building up the Harvard College Observatory (HCO).

I had no terrors about the Harvard job or anybody connected with it. I had managed for Seares a meeting of the Astronomical Society of the Pacific. He had said to me, "You're in charge of this." That gave me a chance to test myself. I found that I could administer, and people seemed to respect the way I did it. That made it easier to go to Harvard. Also, I had been called upon to give a major lecture for the ASP at San Francisco and to tell about my work, and that also helped me.

Almost at once I felt that I had the Observatory and the other jobs under control, thanks largely to one special gentleman, Solon Bailey. He had been acting director after Pickering died and a member of the staff for some twenty years. When I became director, he did a very noble thing. He said, "I should get off the grounds now. How about sending me down to the observatory station in South America to get observations and straighten things out there? Then I would not be in the way."

That was a very kind suggestion, because one of the hardest things for a new director to do is to get along with those who are no longer doing what they had done. Bailey arranged that he should go to Peru and run the station, and I was able to take over smoothly. He was a very fine gentleman. He and his biologist son Irving were both members of the National Academy of Sciences. Only once since then have there been two members from the same family.

Bailey was a specialist in stellar work, nothing very remarkable; I don't remember any large contribution that he made. His largest contribution so far as I personally was concerned was made when I visited Harvard as a graduate student, and he suggested that I look into globular clusters. Within a month or two after I got to Mount Wilson, Shapley and the globular clusters became synonyms. Bailey showed me that this was a rich field to get into; he also discovered a lot of variable stars.

Among the other staff members when I arrived was E. S. King, a good faithful workman in charge of photographic routines. The business of the Observatory was handled by Mr. Willard Garrish, whose main job was keeping me from spending money too fast.

Then there was Leon Campbell, who was one of the important men at the Observatory, and who was very sympathetic. He was not a trained astronomer—he went to high school but nothing beyond—but he was our contact with the amateur variable star observers and a devoted manager of their affairs for the next thirty years. The American Association for Variable Star Observers was founded at Harvard Observatory in 1911, and at the present time it is still a thriving amateur scientific society. The AAVSO does really good work besides absorbing the energies of amateurs. We got special gifts from amateurs to support it. We didn't spend a great deal of money. We had annual meetings at the Observatory, and many a person remembers Mrs. Shapley entertaining the amateurs and their friends on the observatory lawns.

Building up the AAVSO was really a serious contribution that the Harvard Observatory made to astronomy. Many observatories fear a loss of prestige if they deal with amateurs. We had some difficulties, but we set the pace, and others went along.

There were others on the Observatory staff, but the ones really conspicuous for scientific training were the two women astronomers, Annie J. Cannon and Henrietta S. Leavitt. Miss Leavitt was one of the most important women ever to touch astronomy. She had many handicaps, including deafness, and when I came to Harvard she was dying of cancer, though we didn't mention that. She worked about a year longer—mostly on the Magellanic Clouds, which became one of our major projects. I worked with her on those, but she was not able to do much by that time. One of the few decent things I have done was to call on her on her death bed; it made life so much different, friends said, that the director came to see her.

Miss Cannon's great contribution was her enormous work in cataloguing star spectra. Her work on the Henry Draper Catalogue of spectral types ranked Miss Cannon as one of the leading women astronomers of all time. She was indeed a wonderful person, and she was glad that I was interested in her classifications.

Miss Cannon had a phenomenal memory. When I went to her office the first day I asked her, "What are you going to do about a star that has spectrum A one time, and F another, and something else a third time—a changing spectrum?" She said, "They're a terrible nuisance, and how can one classify things if they are not going to stay put?" "Well," I said, "anyway I'd like to see the spectrum of SW Andromedae." (That was a faint variable-star spectrum that I had a hunch about.) She called to her assistant: "Will you get Plate I 37311?" She just sang out that five-figure number. The girl went to the stacks and got the plate and SW Andromedae was on it!

She was good at numbers. The spectrum catalogue was her job; mine was getting the money to publish the ten quarto volumes. That money came from nice friends, mostly her own. As far as the spectra went, I was her assistant. I encouraged the work, while she used her wonderful eyesight and memory to go on classifying the magnitudes and the spectra and the positions of stars down to the ninth magnitude (covering the whole sky). When she had finished the Henry Draper Catalogue (HD), we talked it over and decided to do an extension—so the HDE was born. It started with work on the spectra of faint Milky Way stars. In that assignment she did nearly 50,000 spectra in addition to the 225,000 she had done in the major HD Catalogue. The extension was for the stars that I thought were the most important in studies of stellar distribution, but they are important in many other ways.

Annie J. Cannon's work was one of Harvard's major contributions. That kind of research was not carried on at Mount

Wilson. There they worked more or less on individual stars. Miss Cannon had the disadvantage—or advantage—of having had some kind of infection while she was in college, and as a result her hearing was pretty much lost. That handicap took her out of the social life and put her into science. In some ways I feel rather grateful to that particular bug.

Soon after I came to Harvard I gave a colloquium; the Harvard people hadn't heard me talk before, so I "put on an act." I'm afraid it was a bit too good. What I mean is that they thought, "Mr. Shapley is clever and he's showing off." I had that feeling because Julian Coolidge, who was expected by some to become director of the Observatory, wrote me a letter afterward saying, "This was very good, but you didn't need to be funny."

The great Charles William Eliot, who was president of Harvard before A. Lawrence Lowell, heard me that time, and again soon after at the American Academy of Arts and Sciences, where I rather "wowed" the audience, because there is so much absurdity about man and the universe that it makes a person laugh just to think about it. The universe is so good and so big, and has so much to it, you don't have to jazz it up. Anyway, when the lecture was over, the mighty and wonderful Dr. Eliot came up and thanked me. "You're a very young man," he said, "and you have a grand subject. But you don't need to emphasize it."

I took that as being properly spanked, which I was. The point was that Eliot was amazed at the way the universe was put together. He sent for me once because he was anxious to find out what I thought about the way Harvard University was going. In fact, he came to our house to a Shapley dinner party just a week or two before he died.

Lawrence Lowell was a different kind of person. He did

not have much respect for science, but he did respect scientists. I could get nearly anything I wanted from him because I was a scientist who talked and who had some respect for government and history.

Harvard Observatory was not at first a very lively place. It was steady, and its ambitions were proper, but the work did not take a lot of brains or manpower. I got into the program and at once commenced doing such things as getting the parallaxes of stars by studying their spectra, and analyzing the variable stars, and especially working on star clusters. As I have mentioned, at Mount Wilson I had already done quite a job on star clusters, getting their distances, and using their distribution as an indication of the size of the Milky Way and its arrangement. In fact, I had done my main work on locating man in the galactic system before I came to Harvard. Sometimes I have thought that anything I did after that was anticlimactic.

Miss Leavitt had done some work on variables earlier, and when I came we put our skills into it. I talked to some friends, made some new acquaintances, and took away some of their spare money to buy girl-hours for these jobs. The variables require a tremendous amount of measuring. I invented the term "girl-hour" for the time spent by the assistants. Some jobs even took several kilo-girl-hours. Luckily Harvard College was swarming with cheap assistants; that was how we got things done. At Mount Wilson one was expected to do all one's own measuring—though I finally had one full-time assistant.

In the 1920s there were not too many places where students could get graduate degrees in astronomy. They could do what I did—go to Princeton, where Russell was. Or they could go to the University of California at Berkeley, or to the

University of Michigan. There were one or two Ph.D.s given at Yerkes Observatory, but that was not then so good.

The Harvard Observatory had very little contact with the University until I had been there two or three years. We had no students, we did no teaching, and Charles Wheeler Willson, the one man who taught elementary astronomy at the University, did not associate himself with the Observatory. Such a situation was not unusual at Harvard. In biology, botany, and zoology the University was always dominantly interested in research. A good deal of Harvard University was not a teaching institution, then or even now. The Observatory was not involved in instruction but rather in the production of knowledge. But the fact that I was called to Harvard shows the flaw in the method. President Lowell deplored the fact that under Pickering astronomy had been managed in such a way that they could not find a successor for him among their own graduates. They had to go out and get a Missourian fresh from California.

Nobody had taken a doctor's degree in astronomy at Harvard until after I came. Then, in the interval from about 1930 to 1945, one-third of all the doctoral degrees given in astronomy in the United States were from Harvard Observatory. One of my early trips abroad got us our very first graduate student, Cecilia Payne. I was in England early in the 1920s and gave a lecture at the Royal Astronomical Society and one to the amateur society, the British Astronomical Association, on galaxies, or stellar evolution, or something of the kind. There was a tall young woman of twenty-five or so who just drank it in. She told me afterward, "I went back to Cambridge and told Professor [Sir Arthur] Eddington that I wanted to study with Harlow Shapley."

She made that decision public, and somebody let us

know. A fellowship was provided, and she came over, incited by that one lecture. Of course, the way I talked about astronomy at that time was somewhat different from the way we talk now. Then there was quite a thrill in the fact that a globular cluster is not next door but is 150,000 million million miles away. It was dazzle talk.

Cecilia Payne (now Cecilia Payne-Gaposchkin) was and is a genius type of person. She got our first doctor's degree in astronomy by applying some brand-new astrophysical ideas to stellar spectra. She showed that, in spite of the diversity of spectral types, stars are pretty much all made of the same atoms. She is one of the two or three leading women astronomers of the world and has been for the past thirty years. Her husband, Sergei Gaposchkin, is also an astronomer, and they have one lovely daughter and two big sons. She can write beautifully; she can also lecture beautifully. She lectures over the country, writes books, and does much research. Currently she and her husband are hot on the subject of the Magellanic Clouds and are doing a tremendous study.

In the late 1920s we had nearly a dozen graduate students. As I said, Cecilia Payne was our first Ph.D., in 1925. In 1928 I invited Harry H. Plaskett to start a graduate department in astronomy and astrophysics, but soon after the program got off the ground he left to become Savilian Professor of Astronomy at Oxford. Our second Ph.D. was Frank Hogg of Canada, in 1929; he wrote on stellar spectrophotometry. After that the students kept coming. When I look back at the list, I am amazed at how many there were. Harvard really had a sort of control of American astronomy. Much of that was due to Bart J. Bok, but of course I hired him. Bok was a Dutchman who came in 1929. I helped him get a nice wife, who is also an astronomer. Bok developed methods of analysis for the study of the dust in space, the interstellar stuff, and that led into types of work we had not done before and helped us to understand our own Milky Way system.

In 1932 we added two more key men to the staff. One was Donald H. Menzel, a student of Russell's at Princeton who had gone on to Lick Observatory—an excellent man who was deep in solar work and very good at it. He also could help from an astrophysical standpoint. He was one of the first to realize that stars were made mostly of hydrogen. During the 1930s he worked with two of our best graduate students, Lawrence Aller and James Baker, on the astrophysics of gaseous nebulae. It was a landmark study, recently reprinted.

Fred Whipple also came from Lick Observatory the same year, another excellent man with a fine critical mind. Whipple was a comet man—he found his first comet on the Harvard Observatory sky patrol plates in 1932, and he went on to discover half a dozen more in the 1930s and early 1940s. He also made great progress in the study of meteors.

Along about 1930 there was a high point (I hope they are keeping it high now) in Harvard Observatory's influence and in its training of people and in its joy of life. That was a time of much social collaboration among us. We used the director's residence (our house) for musicales and plays. We played deck tennis; I was the best doggoned player in the whole bunch, because, as they pointed out, "He's the director. He looks this way, but he's hitting it that way." I could beat them all until Leo Goldberg came along as a graduate student in the mid-1930s. By and by Goldberg became director of the University of Michigan Observatory, and now he is director of Harvard Observatory itself.

The period when we were building up the program was a time of "boom" in science generally. F. A. Saunders and Theodore Lyman were in physics at Harvard; they couldn't touch the modern physics, but they were lively. They could collaborate with us; we could collaborate with them. I knew the zoologist George H. Parker and the geologist Reginald Daly very well on account of being touched that way. They were able men and nationally renowned.

At Harvard in the early 1930s we covered almost all fields, and that was when the graduate students commenced flooding in—including a number of foreigners. I had got into the habit of going abroad and in consequence foreign students naturally came to Harvard. Once Warren Weaver, Director for Natural Science at the Rockefeller Foundation, speaking to a group in New York when I happened to be with him, said, "You know, at the Foundation we call Harvard the broken English observatory." I have a picture from that period showing fourteen people from fourteen different institutions, all of them then doing graduate work at Harvard or having done it. The nationalities were Dutch, Russian, Turkish, Belgian, Mexican, British, Irish, Canadian, Finnish, Czech, Italian, German, and Japanese.

When I really got into things, I found I doing four or five different major jobs—administration, fund-raising (which included public speaking), building up a staff, and finding graduate students. Getting the money and increasing the staff were important. I did some public speaking in the early days to raise money; later I did much more. I enjoyed that because I was pretty good at it. I could tell people great things. It was joyous to me to bring new knowledge on a grand scale to people who wanted to listen; so I had many invitations to speak.

As for the fund raising, they said that people generally crossed to the other side of the street when they saw me coming. I remember Walter Adams once telling me at Mount Wilson that raising money is a low form of art; so he had me do it because I could fit into the begging scheme better than he could. We raised the money for Harvard as gifts—some from the Agassizes and the Weyerhausers, and miscellaneous kinds of people who could give us some money without feeling it. We needed money for specific projects, and there was also the continual drive to raise money for endowment for the Observatory. The endowment for research at the Observatory was at first about a million dollars; I got it up to two or three million before very long. We were not a big operation. It seems to me that we got along on very little money. Astronomers have never been highly paid, and I think I was able to convince my colleagues that we should not work for money—we should work for the glory of the contribution.

In all this I have not said much about the major research projects that were going on at the Harvard Observatory, but I was in the thick of them and they were worthwhile enterprises.

The work on the Magellanic Clouds had been started by Miss Leavitt, as I said earlier. She had discovered a great many variable stars in the Magellanic Clouds, and naturally I was interested in their periods and magnitudes. I plunged into it, with help, studying the Magellanic Cloud challenge almost from the beginning of my Harvard program.

The Magellanic Clouds are important because they are a pair of irregular galaxies only about 180,000 light-years away —in other words, they are near at hand and much can be learned from them, including facts about ordinary giant stars and a great deal about our own galactic system. The period-luminosity relation of the Cepheid variables, so crucial for my Mount Wilson work, had been uncovered first in the Magellanic Clouds.

For about three decades, beginning in 1922, I was known as "Mr. Magellanic Clouds." During that time we managed to double the number of known variable stars—the "we" including my helpful assistants, foremost among whom were Jenka Mohr, Sylvia Mussells, and Virginia McKibben Nail. Approximately 2 percent of the supergiant stars in the Clouds are variable. Along the way I noticed a curious and still-unexplained phenomenon: in the Small Cloud one quarter of the Cepheid variables pulsate with periods between one and two days, compared to only 1.5 percent in the Large Cloud.

One of my favorite stars is in the Large Magellanic Cloud —the blue supergiant S Doradus. My studies revealed that its intrinsic brightness is nearly a million times greater than the sun; in fact, it is the most luminous star known. Although S Doradus is a pretty large star—it could swallow up the entire earth's orbit—there are some neighboring red supergiants in the Large Cloud that could even engulf the orbit of Jupiter.

Strange as it may seem, until recently the great majority of the studies of these Southern Hemisphere objects were carried out in the Northern Hemisphere at Harvard. This was possible because Harvard Observatory had a long history of operating a southern station. The Harvard observing station in Arequipa, Peru, was started about 1890 and was operated with only a few small telescopes. Bailey had found the first good location for a station; he had gone down there for the first time in 1889. When he went back after I became director, he was in charge of the two or three Peruvians who were helping us get photographic plates on the Magellanic Clouds.

The programs were planned in Cambridge and sent on to Peru (later, when we moved the station, to South Africa) and the exposed plates were sent back.

Very little analysis was done in the Southern Hemisphere until I had been at Harvard fifteen or twenty years. The system was to have a careful observer—when we could find one—make observations according to the schedules, then have all the analysis and study done in Cambridge. To get more material on the variable stars in the Magellanic Clouds we would send instructions to our Boyden Station in the Southern Hemisphere to make more plates of different kinds and different exposures. Instead of having only four or five plates, which are not enough to give good light curves of the stars, we could increase the attack to a hundred plates. Then we could get accurate periods and light curves and find more variables. When I say we plunged into a task of that kind, I mean that we got much more material to analyze.

In 1927 we decided to transfer the southern station to South Africa. There were several reasons for the decision. One was that we expected better atmospheric conditions for observing, though actually they proved very little better. Another was that we thought we could get money in and out of South Africa better. In Peru we were dealing with a difficult type of government, and we had to work on a sort of bribery system. Another reason for the change was that it gave us a good argument to the Rockefeller Foundation for a big telescope at a new site.

We had good reports on atmospheric conditions in various places, reports from meteorological explorations in addition to earlier ones by Bailey. We tried out northern Chile twice, in two different seasons. The station had to be at a considerable altitude—say 5,000 to 6,000 feet—and it had to be under the southern part of the sky because the bright stars that we especially wanted to study are there. Miss Cannon said that some of the plates were the best she had ever seen for classifying spectra. That area has a very steady sky. Still, the Chilean locations were isolated, and at that time it was hard to find brave people to go down and stick it out. So one reason for not choosing Chile was that living conditions were bad. In South Africa the observers were not so isolated. Nowadays airplanes negate some of those difficulties. And anyway we astronomers are heroes. We will suffer. We will be happy to go in the interest of the bright, wonderful display of stars.

When we sent equipment to South Africa in 1927, we stopped tentatively near Bloemfontein, with the expectation of moving on. But the station has remained there ever since. It has been about the best astronomical site in the world—better than any in the Northern Hemisphere. That is because of dry conditions and the rather high altitude. So our early choice was a pretty good one, though conditions are better in some places in northern Chile.

From the time the station was moved to South Africa, and even for a while in Peru, we were fortunate in having John S. Paraskevopoulos, a Greek-born astronomer, to head it. He served as superintendent until his death in 1951.

Besides the Magellanic Clouds, we started work on the more distant galaxies—mostly statistically, studying them by the tens of thousands. Around the turn of the century the Danish astronomer J. L. E. Dreyer had compiled a list of 13,226 nebulae and clusters in the *New General Catalogue* and two *Index Catalogues*. Various investigators had attempted to sort out the starry galaxies from the gaseous nebulae and star clusters and everything else, but the material was far from homogeneous. We recognized this unevenness, and one of our top assistants, Adelaide Ames, helped me make a more systematic preliminary survey of 1249 bright galaxies. The Shapley-Ames Catalogue was rather useful; it has recently been brought up to date by the French-born astronomer Gerard de Vaucouleurs.

Miss Ames was an able and sympathetic person. She knew that I had plenty of headaches at that time (it was 1932) arranging for the International Astronomical Union meeting, so she took over much of the work on the catalogue and the IAU arrangements. It was a great shock when she was drowned in an accident that June.

As I said, much of our work on the galaxies was statistical —investigating, for example, the remarkable nest of hundreds of galaxies around the region of the north pole of the Milky Way. We also used counts of galaxies to detect the borders of the Milky Way. Where the Milky Way is very smoggy from interstellar dust, the distant galaxies are just blocked out and their numbers drop off. But we also found some surprisingly transparent patches near the Milky Way— "windows," we call them. These windows allowed us to explore to great distances along the plane of the Milky Way, and in that fashion we got some variable stars even on the other side of our galaxy's nucleus in Sagittarius. Otherwise it was too cosmically smoggy to see stars in the nucleus itself.

Sometimes we did study individual galaxies. We were taken by surprise in 1938 when a plate from South Africa showed unexpectedly and almost accidentally an entirely new type of galaxy. The plate, which was made with the 24-inch Bruce telescope, showed a couple of thousand faint and distant galaxies as well as about thirty thousand intervening stars of our galactic system. The assistant who was inspecting the plate thought at first it had been spoiled by a darkroom disaster, a careless thumbprint right in the middle. A more detailed look showed a swarm of faint star images in the constellation Sculptor.

Our suspicions that the Sculptor cluster might be spurious disappeared when we found confirmation on a 1908 plate which Bailey had taken when he was on a site-testing expedition to South Africa. His photograph had a total exposure of 23 hours and 16 minutes, and it was made on the best parts of five consecutive nights. The Sculptor system turned out to be the first example of a dwarf galaxy. Soon after finding this one, we got another in the constellation Fornax.

When I came to Harvard, the equipment at the Observatory was in a rather bad way. One of the first jobs was to build it up in order to work on the galaxies and the Milky Way. We made changes in instruments and got many more telescopes, including a 61-inch for South Africa and another for the Northern Hemisphere. When I came, our Northern Hemisphere telescopes were all in Cambridge. Eventually we looked for a better location, away from the city lights, but near enough that the graduate students could easily go out for observing. That is why we started the Oak Ridge Station, about twenty-five miles from Harvard, around 1930.

The Astronomer Royal, Sir Frank Dyson, came over from England in 1932 to dedicate the 61-inch telescope at the Oak Ridge Station and to plant a cornerstone. That was at the time of a total solar eclipse in New England, so the International Astronomical Union Congress was also held at Harvard, in early September. Eddington came to New England for the total solar eclipse and then came to Harvard afterward for the IAU meeting. I tried to get him to give a lecture on stellar interiors and he said, "I've given that lecture once, so I won't do it any more. I have nothing new to add." That annoyed me a little, but he was right. So many of us—I won't mention names—give the same lecture over and over.

Looking back on the whole Harvard period, I think I would say that its peak came in about 1932. Several things happened that year. I was offered three or four university presidencies; I was decorated by Harvard, and also received some foreign honors; I traveled abroad; we had some very good students going. That was also the year of the New England eclipse, the IAU meeting, and Adelaide Ames's death. All in all, 1932 stands out in my memory because so many things were going on. I sometimes wonder what I did afterward, but of course I have already described some of it and there was more to come.

Chapter Eight

A FEW EXTRACURRICULAR
ACTIVITIES

Along with running the Harvard Observatory I was involved in a number of extracurricular projects, some not related to the job, but others rather closely connected with it.

When I was first at Harvard I gave the Lowell Lectures, as a good many Harvard professors do. I had an advantage over others in novelty of subject matter—cosmic evolution, galaxies, and variable stars. I kept the lecture hall exactly full for all eight lectures. The lectures, I was told, should last precisely one hour. I finished the eighth one with fourteen seconds to spare. "I must stop now with one concluding query: Is this a world of *chance* or a world of *choice?*" There was no time for an answer. I made a dignified bow and walked off the platform exactly on the second.

In consequence, I had one of the most ridiculous pay-offs. I was in Bombay many years later, attending a dinner for visitors from abroad. I had come in with the Astronomer Royal. Across the table from me was a blond lady, very, very blond. With her was a dark-skinned Hindu, very, very dark. They were soon looking at me and talking about me. Finally they told me who I was. I had to admit it; the Astronomer Royal was there. "But how do you know me?" I asked.

The lady said, "I heard your lectures in Boston." (I identified these as the Lowell series.) "I went to all of them," she said. "After each lecture I went to the Public Library and walked home with a young man. And here we are. We are still walking together. You raised that question, 'Is this a world of chance or a world of choice?' You didn't tell us. We talked it over and decided that it was a world of choice; so we got married."

Early in 1930 the American Astronomical Society had a meeting at the Harvard College Observatory, and the Observatory put on the *Harvard Observatory Pinafore*—a parody. There were enough people and enough dramatic talent around the place for theatricals, but even so, the *Pinafore* show was quite a stunt for us to carry through. Many critics consider it tops in the performances at Harvard Observatory. We happened to have some competent musicians on the staff and some fairly good voices. I was, naturally, the director and the producer, but I had very good cooperation in the music and the drama parts of it. We did it so well for the American Astronomical Society that the local scientists asked us to repeat it for the Bond Astronomical Club, a group of amateurs that meet at HCO. The second time we did it a good deal better, we thought. Of course it was a *tour de force*, the whole thing, but it was fun, and it tied the Observatory together as nothing else has ever done.

H.M.S. Pinafore, the original, was first produced in 1878, and after that *Pinafore* parodies swept the country. Winslow Upton, an astronomer who was at Harvard then (he went to Brown University later), wrote this one. We put it on in the Observatory with all its jests and jokes and catchy tunes and phrases. The astronomer was told that

"His knee should bend and his neck should curl,
His back should twist and his face should scowl,

One eye should squint and the other protrude,
And this should be his customary attitude."

Various writers have reproduced some of the songs. I
recently saw a copy with half a dozen of the most absurd
songs. So it is "in the literature," but hard to find.

At the Shapley house we held numerous musical eve-
nings. One of these was especially notable because Albert Einstein took part. It came about in this way. Harvard University
was planning to celebrate its Tercentenary in 1936, and sixty
leading scholars from all over the world were to be invited. I
headed a subcommittee to choose those from the physical sciences who should be so honored. The subcommittee agreed
that Einstein was an obvious first selection, but we also agreed
that if he came he would steal the show.

This created a crisis of a sort, but fortunately I had a
bright idea: we could invite Einstein to come in 1935 to receive an honorary degree and thus get him out of the way of
the Tercentenary, leaving our celebration undisturbed by the
madness which at that time hung around the name of Einstein.

The Harvard management was delighted with my
scheme. I wrote to Einstein and at the same time Mrs. Shapley
wrote to Mrs. Einstein. The letters intimated that Einstein
was being invited to Harvard for an honorary degree and
suggested that he might like to stay at our house, where he
would be protected from reporters and the curious public.
"And, Dr. Einstein, if you can come on that date, will you
please bring your violin, and we will have a dinner party and
an evening devoted to chamber music?"

By return mail came the answer: "I am coming and I

shall gladly bring my violin." We had taken advantage of his weakness. It was Bach and Brahms and their kind that he wanted to meet at the Observatory residence.

Mrs. Einstein was unable to come because of a death in her family. "But take good care of Albert," she wrote. "He is a sensitive plant. He should smoke no cigar. He can have coffee for breakfast, but in the evening he must have Sanka; otherwise he will not sleep well."

Einstein followed his instructions. When we rose from the dinner table and the men went into the library, he said "no" to the proffered cigar. Sadly he got out his pipe. Later I tempted him again. This time he took a cigar, saying softly, "Ach, mein Weib!"

The music went along successfully for about three hours, Einstein playing in whatever grouping was suggested, obviously happy. But bedtime was approaching. As manager I rapped on a music stand. "It has been a lot of fun, but Albert and Carl must go to bed now" (Carl being the current *natu minimus*). The fiddlers began sorting out the music, upsetting music stands, having a beautiful time at the end of a chamber-music evening. With some respect for my urging they started to leave, but not rapidly. Who would want to go away hastily from an Einstein evening? He might say something—and indeed he did. He whispered it to me as I was sending the fiddlers along. "They remind me of time," he said.

"But it is only eleven o'clock. The time is not late; they will be gone in a few minutes."

"But they remind me of time," he persisted.

"How so?"

"Always going—but never gone."

We did other things around the Observatory that were not quite along the lines of astronomical deduction or induction, or the making of measures, and the discussion of measures. For instance, there was the Full Moonatics Club, and operation that we carried on for a few years in the late 1940s. It was called that because when the moon is full and the sky is light you can't make good astrophotographs, so during the two or three nights around the full of the moon you make wild theories instead. The club met on call in our house, with soft drinks. About fifteen of the graduate students, mostly men, would attend, and there we did some rather funny tricks. One was that somebody would take at random a statement from a standard astronomy textbook like the one by Russell, Dugan, and Stewart—a statement about Venus, for example, and say, "That was written thirty years ago. What do we think about that now? What shall we do to interpret Venus (or whatever it was) better? Let us improve this text." A collection of notebooks on the Full Moonatics meetings has survived.

It was a good deal of fun. Two or three girl students attended, but they did not help very much. Some of the boys would not speak out either. They seemed frightened. I remember one who is now rather important in astronomy—he is a member of the council of the American Astronomical Society—whom I could not get to come through at all. Maybe he was shy.

I tried out group thinking with the Full Moonatics. Lyman Bryson of Columbia University wondered if it would be possible to get a group of good thinkers together and have them think in a new and different pattern. This was not just to make an accumulation of individual thoughts, but to develop an entirely new thought pattern. We tried it, and though nothing significant came out of it, at least it was an attempt to see what could be done with integrated thinking.

More important than the Full Moonatics meetings were the Hollow Square sessions in the Observatory library. A number of people knew the Harvard Observatory only through those sessions. We would all get together, about thirty or more people—staff and graduate students and also others who knew answers and knew how to ask questions—around a big square with the center empty. The advantage of these gatherings over the colloquia was that, by the rules, the subject had to be changed every ten minutes. That rule kept some people from talking too long, and incited others to try a shortie.

The Hollow Squares went on year after year in the 1930s and the 1940s. They were held about every two weeks or so, depending on the breaks in the work and the breaks in the news. Generally three or four topics would pop up. If a person had just got a measure of a peculiar variable star, he would show it around. It was a very informal exhibit. We kept it lively, and also moderately humorous. We would josh colleagues and josh ourselves. Many loose ideas came out of the Hollow Squares—ideas that were better than those from the stodgy colloquia. At the colloquia every week or two there was a formal presentation—one man would get up and harangue the whole group. At the Hollow Squares nobody talked indefinitely.

The Hollow Squares were about the best group operation we had. Some rather good discoveries and developments first came out in those discussions. It was not all spontaneous; I would send a scout around to see what was about to burst loose that we could talk about. I might send a note to somebody like Dr. Bart Bok: "We must have your view of the spectroscopic parallaxes, and I'm going to ask about it at the Hollow Square." Then he would come loaded. Sometimes visiting astronomers came to the Hollow Squares. That helped a good deal, especially if they were the kind you could rib a little. The meetings lasted about an hour, and no records were kept—that would have spoiled the informality.

When I retired as director of the Observatory, there was concern as to whether the Hollow Squares would go on or should go on. I was naturally not going to be on hand to run them. I wanted to leave that for the next administration. One Hollow Square was held and it flopped. Maybe there was not enough life in it. They tried to make a variation by having a hollow circle and a hollow triangle, but it didn't work, I am sorry to say.

Rather a different kind of activity—and outside of Harvard—is the Institute on Religion in an Age of Science. After my findings about our peripheral position in our galaxy began to be talked about considerably, the ideas reached the preachers and theologians and worried them a bit. I had conversations with them, and they invited me to come and talk in their churches.

An outcome of that was the formation, about fifteen years ago, of the Institute on Religion in an Age of Science under the umbrella of the American Academy of Arts and Sciences. I was president of it for a while, and I still go to many of the meetings, which are held for about a week in the summer at Star Island, Portsmouth, New Hampshire. At the first meeting some big shots came and gave lectures on or near the subject of science and theology. It was a surprise to Ralph Burhoe, at that time executive officer of the Academy and the father of the operation, that if you invite a good physicist to talk about religion and what it means, he will perform. With the Institute we touched a sensitive point in men's thinking.

I put some of the lectures that were given at Portsmouth into a book, *Science Ponders Religion* (1960). Now the Institute has started a magazine; it has a fancy Greek name— *Zygon,* meaning "yoke," in reference to the joining of science and religion. I think it will succeed. The Meadville Theological School at the University of Chicago helps with it. This confronting of religion and science is a notable thing to do, but I am not very good at it; I don't know enough of the language of metaphysics or theology. I can worry people about what I don't know, but that is all. There are some good essays in *Science Ponders Religion.* In the companion book, *Religion Ponders Science* (1964), some of the essays are also good but most of them were written by theologians, who did not have very effective material. Theology is in a bad way.

Getting back to science, I have been on the executive board of Science Service for more than thirty years and was at one of the meetings that led to its establishment. That was back in 1920. George Ellery Hale and E. W. Scripps met at Scripps' house near San Diego, California, to talk over the possibility of better reporting of science, chiefly in the newspapers. Scripps was interested in this and was willing to give money for it. Hale felt strongly about the poor reporting of astronomy: the subject was so sensational that it made some of the reporters write startling headlines, and Hale had got pretty well fed up.

Hale asked me to go to a meeting with Scripps because he knew I had some journalism experience and also that I could take down the discussion in shorthand. I was glad to be invited. I would do anything Hale suggested, because he was recognized as a wise person. Also I was a little homesick for my newspaper career way back before I went to Missouri University. Besides, the idea was obviously a good one, and I had already been encouraging writing on science.

Professor William Ritter, who became the first head of Science Service, was also in the party. It was a meeting that was typical for Scripps. He was a wild man or a great man, or both, depending on your point of view. He enjoyed himself, I could see that, just telling Mr. Ritter what a nincompoop he was. He enjoyed abusing the man right there. I have known one or two other people who worked that way. But it was embarrassing both to Mr. Hale and to me. We did succeed in outlining how we would go about setting up a science reporting business. Ritter was made nominal head. Later Watson Davis, a student of engineering and reporting, got into the game and in 1931 became the director. That was also the beginning of *Science News Letter,* Science Service's publication now called *Science News.* The operation succeeded because Scripps gave about $500,000 as an endowment, providing an income of $30,000 a year. It influenced the other journals. *The New York Times* and the *Tribune* and the *World* soon had science editors; Science Service had pointed the way. So it was a pretty successful enterprise.

It was nonprofit, and it wasn't hard to make it nonprofit. We had to work hard at first to get newspapers to take the telegraphic service. I worked rather closely with it until the last two or three years. E. G. Sherburne, Jr., is now the head of Science Service. I was on the committee for the selection. Science Service has about fifty people working for it in Washington, D.C. It has a good man at the head and many experienced writers on the staff. More money is needed for salaries because over the years Science Service has trained writers well and then lost them to magazines or newspapers. That was good, of course, but it made the operation difficult to manage. But some writers have been with Science Service ten or twenty years.

I was president of Science Service for some years, and the president from 1954 to 1967 was Leonard Carmichael, the head of the Smithsonian Institution, who then became vice president for research of the National Geographic Society. Glenn T. Seaborg, chairman of the U.S. Atomic Energy Commission, is now president.

Science Service has done other valuable things, among them the Science Talent Search. This was more or less invented by G. Edward Pendray of Westinghouse, at a meeting with Watson Davis and me in New York City, where we discussed ways of locating talented science students the country over. Westinghouse puts up money for it. We select forty students a year. While we have dug up a lot of science talent, I don't think Einstein could have made it because we don't have a submerged-genius category. But nearly all of our winners go on to become doctors of science. Apparently we have made very few mistakes. The students go to Washington for four or five days of interviews about the first of March every year. The proceedings include what is probably the most outstanding scientific dinner given in Washington. Six hundred people attend and such "big" people as Vannevar Bush and Alan T. Waterman have been speakers.

Perhaps the most important thing that Science Service has sponsored is the science fairs. There had been a few such fairs, but the operation got constructively organized only when Science Service took it over. One of the first fairs, which more or less started the movement, was at Providence, Rhode Island, where all the schools including the parochial schools were invited to take part. A newspaper underwrote the expenses, which were only a few hundred dollars. There were eleven hundred exhibits. The Fair's success amazed everybody. At that Fair I looked at all the exhibits; nearly always there was a mother or an Uncle Joe or an Aunt Emma swelling with pride because their boy had this exhibit synthesizing silk, or whatever it was. The fairs were for the community, and they have remained a community operation.

Now there are thousands of science fairs, held all over the country—first in the grade schools, and then in the high schools—and a national fair as well. Nationally famous scientists judge the big exhibits. Each year there are thousands of exhibits—too many to begin with; we have to cut them down by selection, going step by step until we get about 425 of the best at Science Service's International Science Fair.

I don't think there is much to the idea that the science fairs diminish interest in other aspects of scholarship. The brightest boys and girls are not all scientifically touched; some are touched in other ways, historically, for instance. A good friend of mine has said, "You scientific people are sapping off the top brains and leaving us with the numskulls." I asked him if they had tried the talent-search experiment. He said, "No, but we don't have any Westinghouse around with $30,000 a year to help us put this show on the road." I told him I would do it for half that price if they wanted me to, but nothing came of it. That was the only criticism of our operation that I have heard.

I was early elected a member of the American Academy of Arts and Sciences, which was at that time largely a Boston and Massachusetts affair. In the early 1940s, when I was president and Hudson Hoagland of Worcester was secretary, we tried to put some life into it. I thought it should have a wider spread. In the Academy there were many good noble people, but they got up only slapdash types of programs. We started to change things. For instance, we had (and do even now) lively meetings eight months of the year. The American Academy, close to Massachusetts Institute of Technology and Harvard and Boston University and other educational institutions, has the manpower and the interest to have that many good meetings. A number of people worked on this; I should not take too much of the credit. One was Edwin Land, an industrialist and a neighbor of mine in New Hampshire, who was president for three years. Soon the Academy began to revitalize itself in many ways. For instance, Kirtley F. Mather, the Harvard geologist, and Howard Mumford Jones, also of Harvard but in the humanities, arranged to get a full-time executive officer for us. Now the Academy does quite remarkable things in the way of special studies of disarmament, science and culture, leadership, and the future.

Hoagland and I almost got a new Academy quarterly started twenty years ago, but one thing and another, like a war, got in the way. In 1955 *Daedalus* was begun, but only in 1958, under the editorship of Gerald Holton, did it become finally and firmly established in its present format. In only a decade it has become a very important periodical.

We looked long for a name that would represent a tie-up of the sciences and the arts. There was a quarterly already, called *The Proceedings of the American Academy of Arts and*

Sciences, but we thought we might do better than that. Resurrecting the earlier Hoagland-Shapley thoughts, I argued for a snappy name. A journal needs one. You do not want to say "The Academy's Proceedings for 1969," or some such dullness. Some members liked "Minerva," but that and similar classical names were already assigned to the satellites in the sky, or to asteroids. Fancy names had been used up. But I found that the name Daedalus had not been used, and it was very appropriate because Daedalus and his son Icarus were aviators, technicians, and experimenters. One of the large fungi is called *Daedalus quercina,* so the name would appeal to botanists. It would cover engineering and pure science and applied science and mythology. So I proposed at a meeting, "How about 'Daedalus'? You probably won't want it because you would not know whether to say Dĕdelus, or Dādelus, or Dēdelus." Fortunately the president at that time was a classicist at Harvard, and he thought mine was quite an ingenious idea. Soon several were talking for Dēdalus. Finally the treasurer of the Academy, from M.I.T., made a motion. "Let's call it Daedalus unless we find some reason not to." So we just sort of bulled it through. The magazine has become accepted, and now has a circulation of about 60,000. Nearly every quarterly issue has also been published as a hard-cover book.

Along with the work of the American Academy of Arts and Sciences, I have been active in Sigma Xi, the scientific honor society. In Sigma Xi I was chairman of the first chapter at Harvard and have been national president. At the present time, one of the Boy Scout things I do is chairing the committee of Sigma Xi that makes grants in aid of research. I have been chairman for about twenty years. We have three meetings a year and distribute about $75,000 annually.

I have also been active in the American Philosophical Society. The Society distributes more than $400,000 a year in grants. It is the richest scholarly society in the world, even the Royal Society does not have as much money. The American Philosophical Society has an endowment of something like $26 million, partly from Eldredge Reeves Johnson, the Victor Records "Master's Voice" man, but mostly from a wealthy Philadelphia doctor named Richard Penrose. For years I have helped distribute the research grants, which are given five times a year. It is hard work to read several hundred research proposals annually. We have to watch it or the tax collector will come and get us; the Society can be tax-free only so long as it is wholly charitable. Not many grants are given in the sciences because scientists can get bigger money from the National Science Foundation, but the Society gives funds for travel expenses for professors in the humanities and for biographies and things of that kind. People generally ask for twice as much as it can afford to give, but the committee knows how to pare the requests down. There are about ten of us on the committee, all hard-boiled old-timers who know when an application is padded.

Long before Hudson Hoagland and I worked together to liven up the American Academy of Arts and Sciences I had known him at Harvard. He was a graduate student when I became director of the Observatory, and a very live one. A small group of instructors at Harvard who were investigating the medium, Margery Crandon, asked if I would come as an expert scientist to observe these goings on—where you sit in the dim light with soft music playing, and ectoplasm terminals go in and out of the medium's body, wander around, ring bells and whistle and do all that wonderful stuff. So I went to a seance in Hoagland's house in Cambridge. My Hudson

Hoagland contact was psychotherapy of a sort—just tom-foolery. But we enjoyed it, and he wrote it up recently. Margery said we were all crooks, thieves, and liars—disreputable!

Some years later Hoagland and his colleague Dr. Gregory Pincus asked me if I would be president of the board of trustees of a new Worcester Foundation for Experimental Biology. I said yes, happily. They wanted to cut loose from Clark University and set up an independent research organization. They knew where they could get a house—a large house that a wholesale plumber was not using—in Shrewsbury, Massachusetts, a suburb of Worcester. I was willing to go along with them because I was interested in the type of work they were doing. One of the main reasons they wanted me was that they thought I could raise some money for them. We organized. We sold the people of Worcester on one particular argument—namely, you give money to the Girl Scouts and you give money for the wonderful concerts and you give money for scientific displays—museums; then why not for research? Why not study hormones? They didn't exactly know what hormones were. I didn't know very well myself. But the citizens came through with the cash. Our ambition was to have half a dozen research scientists and some assistants and a budget of $25,000 a year or more. That was ambitious in those days.

My job was partly meeting with groups and getting gifts or encouraging gifts. With the help of a local rabbi we did a pretty good job. Soon we found we had real money, and we kept getting more. We got grants from the Navy and from the National Science Foundation and from cancer research. We specialized very largely in steroid chemistry. A number of fine things have come out of that work. Now the Foundation's budget is more than $3 million a year, and it has more than one hundred and fifty scientists and many buildings. It has mushroomed. I've been associated with it all the time, first as head of the trustees and in the last ten years or more on the executive committee.

A much earlier money-raising activity was the National Science Fund, in the late 1930s. I not only participated in that, I *was* it, more or less. The National Science Fund was an attempt to get big industry and labor unions to contribute to a great national fund for research in the sciences. It was under the auspices of the National Academy of Sciences, but it hadn't got off the ground before the National Science Foundation was being organized, and I was also in the thick of that. The National Science Fund became quiet, slowed up, died. It was buried at a formal meeting at the Cosmos Club in Washington. I was glad not to have that job to worry about any more.

The National Science Foundation, being a government organization and having to go through Congress, was the first of my extracurricular activities that got into the realm of politics; later others did also. Some of the others were different too, because they were of an international nature.

Chapter Nine

INTERNATIONAL CONTACTS

Early in the 1930s, I worked a good deal on refugee rescue. There were times when I was a little scarce around the Observatory, especially when there were committee meetings in New York to raise money to rescue people from Hitler's grasp. Some of these were famous people—like the climatologist Victor Conrad—who were thrown out, and some of them in a very cruel way. Conrad had been dragged by the beard. I worked on getting funds and on committee operations, trying to rescue them. Nearly a hundred rescues went through or touched my office.

When the United States got into the Second World War, there was much activity around the Observatory. We had special meetings there with the refugees. To be sure, the Federal Bureau of Investigation watched all this, but we didn't worry too much about that. I think we were wise in not worrying too much. We knew that a person who had escaped from an East European country might be tinged with communism. We had a good deal of difficulty with escapees of that kind, but it was a part of the show, and the show paid off well.

There was a social side, too. Around Christmas time there was a celebration at the Observatory residence to which we would invite the refugees. The German and Polish people were especially fond of Christmas ceremonies. The Observatory Christmas parties were happy moments in their lives, they said. In addition, we had non-Christmas parties in the house—dances and games and joys of that kind.

The refugee operation that I started was called the National Research Associates. It was aimed at assisting the older refugee scholars. We worked with the Emergency Committee in Aid of Displaced Foreign Scholars. I was on the executive committee of that New York group. There were other refugee committees as well.

Our job was locating scholars who needed to be rescued, getting them to this country, and when they arrived helping to place them somewhere—finding them jobs. They were all academic people—scientists, historians, political scientists, statisticians. One of the leading workers in mathematical logic in the world today is a man that I helped to get out of Poland with his wife and children. It took nearly three years but we got them out, and the Rockefellers put up the money to get him well located. Because he was so famous, it wasn't hard to relocate him. But that man never acknowledged my help after I had got him out and settled. He never wrote to me. Some people said, "Well, that is what Professor X always does. He never answers letters unless they concern him fiscally." Very recently I happened to meet him and he apologized for not writing to me.

But the Germans and Austrians that we rescued were not embittered. Only one escapee said, "I feel rather obliged to kill someone, but just whom?" Most of them were kindly disposed. It is the choice of God, they said; it is the will of the Almighty that this is the way it is. Some simply quoted, "How odd of God to choose the Jews."

Gradually we used up the money that had been stored in the banks to support the refugees. They died off, one after another, over the years. By the mid-1950s there was only one left, and he was then being supported by his son.

With very few exceptions the people at the Observatory had nothing to do with the refugee operation. They were in war jobs. As the war deepened the Harvard Observatory staff was taking part in a variety of activities. Many were in the optical plant in Brookline, Massachusetts, which was built for lens work. James G. Baker had an important optical job. He and his crew did notable designing of new lenses for war use, some of which were shot down in Germany. Members of the South African staff went to the front and did gun fighting in Ethiopia—of all places. We just kept track of them and saw to it that the jobs were kept open so that they could come back if they wanted to. At the Observatory we went right on with our routine researches. Harvard's biggest war project was the underwater sound laboratory that was built for the Office of Scientific Research and Development (OSRD) and set up by Frederick V. Hunt. But the Observatory had very little connection with OSRD. James B. Conant, then president of Harvard University, was liaison operator, and I was a bit involved through some of my committee jobs.

Mrs. Shapley was for four years an operator in the making of firing tables, and other mathematical tables. This was done at M.I.T. for the Navy and the Air Force. She also helped manage the Observatory. I remember her coming home off the night shift, dog-tired, complaining that she had to leave an eight-inch Navy shell four miles up over the weekend. That was one way we could help the war effort. There is after all much celestial mechanics in shooting, as we now know very well. The astronomers pioneered trajectories.

One of the Observatory's best contributions was in navigation. Donald Menzel, Bart Bok, Frances Wright, and others worked on that. Frances Wright especially was interested in navigation. In fact, she and Bok wrote a successful book, *Navigation,* and there was some teaching of aviators at the Observatory. Bok and I also got out a paperback called *Astronomy from Shipboard.* It was designed to pep up the traveler to the distant battle fronts.

After the war, Charles Smiley at Brown University and I worked on restoring the libraries of the Polish observatories and universities. The German army and the Russian army both went across Poland and tore it all to pieces. We replaced the books by writing to the universities of America, the ones that had big libraries, and asking, "Please send us your duplicates." We raised money for freight and had the books sent to New York. Three or four destroyed libraries were fully restored. I was in Poland in about 1964 and I found that our work was recognized. In fact, there were shelves labeled "books from American universities."

But the most interesting thing I did for the Poles happened soon after the First World War. In about 1922 I was in Rome for a meeting and Professor T. H. Banachiewicz, the leading Polish astronomer of the time, came to me and said, "You have a lot of telescopes at Harvard. We have nothing any more. The war has ruined us."

When I went home I got hold of an 8-inch Bache photographic telescope that had been doing "missionary work" out in Arizona. It had been used to bait a trap so that a Mrs. Steward would give Arizona University an observatory. Before that it had been used at Harvard for some of Miss Cannon's work on spectra. We brought it back from the West, fixed it up, and sent it to Poland. It was promptly used for research at a site south of Krakow, and it has done various good things, such as discovering comets. The Polish government thanked us for it. Three years later the time of the "loan" had expired, and the loan was renewed. Again we got thanks from the Polish parliament. And then we heard from them no more.

Later there was another world war and another destruction of books and telescopes. In 1943 or thereabouts here came this same handsome black-mustached astronomer—Banachiewicz—with a request. Again we mustered our strength and sent another 8-inch telescope. This second 8-inch Bache telescope had been used for most of Miss Cannon's great classification of stellar spectra, which was then finished. We dressed up the telescope and sent it along. It went to Torun in northwest Poland, the place where Copernicus was born. Swedish astronomers assisted in the transfer and got Torun Observatory working on an important program. A Polish woman astronomer, Professor Wilhelmina Iwanowska, one of the leading women astronomers of Europe, has the use of that particular telescope to study spectra. But we can't have any more world wars because Harvard is fresh out of 8-inch telescopes!

There were other things to do for Poland. In 1943, along with President Henry N. MacCracken of Vassar College, I assisted in the celebration of the four-hundredth anniversary of Copernicus's death. That resulted in a big binge in Carnegie Hall. The President of the United States, Franklin D. Roosevelt, sent a message. In fact, I helped write the message that he sent to me. The Polish Ambassador in full grandeur came up from Washington. Carnegie Hall was filled to the rafters. As we were celebrating a revolutionary—namely, Copernicus, who made scientific history with *De revolutionibus orbium coelestium*—we decided to salute some *modern* revolutionaries. The idea came off beautifully because everybody wanted to cooperate. It was for the good of Poland, after all, and we were sentimental.

We selected about half a dozen American revolutionaries to honor, including Albert Einstein, T. H. Morgan, the geneticist, Igor Sikorsky, the helicopter man—he certainly was a revolutionary—and Henry Ford, and two or three others. They were brought to New York and given diplomas on the stage. The great harpsichordist Wanda Landowska was there. I found her difficult to manage. After we had let her take one extra bow or encore, she wanted to do some Polish national music. I had to rise and push her down.

That was one of the few times that Einstein left Princeton. I had decided, as the manager, that we would let two of the neo-revolutionaries make brief speeches; one would be Einstein. The other was to have been Walt Disney, but he couldn't be there, and Deems Taylor gracefully represented him. When I called on Einstein, and motioned that it was time for him to come to the podium to make some remarks, Dr. MacCracken, as my assistant, got confused about the program. He shoved Einstein back into his chair. I came to Einstein's assistance. There was a sort of struggle going on, with me trying to introduce this Einstein revolutionary and MacCracken trying to prevent him from rising.

Finally, Einstein got up and made his speech. It was in broken English, and Einstein's English had been pretty badly broken. He pointed out that it was not inappropriate for him to appear "because Copernicus was the great leader of scientists and he was our teacher"—or some such connection. It was a modest talk in pidgin English and the audience just roared. Carnegie Hall rattled with applause. In the front row were some of my friends from the Century Club. I had sent them tickets so they could come, and they did and applauded wildly. They are of course good Republicans and careful clubmen; that they would applaud this Relativity man and his doings was a little surprising. That night I asked one of them about it and was told: "Well, I think the reason we applauded was that we'd always insisted that we couldn't understand one damn word of this relativity nonsense. And here we heard Relativity himself talking about it and still we couldn't understand it. So we were right. We just can't understand it." The logic was rather peculiar, but anyway they came and applauded.

We also did something toward re-establishing Pulkovo Observatory in Russia. That is now the biggest observatory in Russia, with a staff of about five hundred. I don't know that we were very helpful except diplomatically. There were some scientific contacts after the First World War. Then in 1945, Harold Spencer Jones, the Astronomer Royal, and I were in Russia, and we went out ten or fifteen kilometers from Leningrad to the site on Pulkovo Hill where the observatory had been. It had been knocked to pieces, but they had saved the big lenses and kept their old manuscripts, buried somewhere. As the Germans came up out of Germany into Russia, trying to capture Pulkovo (which they didn't get), they fought and died right around that astronomical observatory.

When we were there after the war the Russians took us to see the remnants so we could help restore the observatory, if we wanted to. But they were proud and could help themselves pretty well, so we weren't much involved after all. At that time they couldn't be expected to progress as fast in astronomical development as we were doing. But a scientist named Maksutov showed me a new kind of lens that he had designed, a double-meniscus, which they were using to spot planes. It had a special adaptation for amateur astronomers. Russia is now the number two country, I would say, in astronomy. America is number one, I modestly point out!

My chief relationship with the Pulkovo Observatory came about in an odd way, and I rather claim credit for having mildly affected the course of Russian astronomy in the past few decades. In the 1930s I received a letter that had come from deep Russia—from Omsk or some other great center. It was in a schoolgirlish type of writing, obviously from a youngster. She said in this letter that her teacher "saw your name in the paper and said I should write to you and then you write to me so that I can learn my English better." Her name was Zdenka Kadla—I think the name is of Czech origin.

After some months I caught up on my correspondence enough to answer her letter, and a few months later another letter came from Zdenka Kadla. We became pen pals. Among other things, she asked me to tell her what I thought of the world and to say whether Russia was a great country. The correspondence went back and forth. We must have exchanged half a dozen letters by 1941. In one of the last that got through she said, "You tell me what you study in your school and I will tell of mine," and she went on to tell about education in Russia.

She got a rather long answer, for a curious reason. The Second World War was going on, though the United States was not yet in it, and travel was very risky. I was in South Africa at our branch observatory and could not fly home. So what did I do but take a boat which took two or three weeks to come up the West African coast. We crossed the Equator, ceremoniously.

Being of a nonsensical nature, I thought, "This is a unique place," and so I wrote letters to my friends: "I am about to cross the Equator and see how the other half looks." I got out my little black book and among the addresses I found Zdenka Kadla of Omsk. So I wrote her about what I did in my school. I described the Harvard Observatory and its research program; I wrote about Miss Cannon and Mrs. Gaposchkin and the staff.

I got home all right, but by then we were in the war. We won the war with the help of the Russians, and Harvard sent me to Russia with fifteen others. Our party arrived at the Moscow airport, where there was a great mob of people and movie cameras ready to shoot—you would have thought it was Ellis Island. Here came the sixteen American scientists. They wouldn't let the first person who dashed off the plane get to the microphone. They said, "We must have the leader." We had fought against the Führer business, but they insisted on having the leader. I had to go off first, for I had "seized control" of our particular delegation in New York, and I was the leader. Being leader means that you make the speeches when you land, and if somebody is ill on the plane you mop up after him. That is what being the leader involves. Anyway, that was my job and I am rather good with a mop.

An official came out and said, "I am the Vice President of the Academy. We would like to have you tell us what you think of the Russian people." I had not had time to plan; I was just getting off the plane from Baku. But I got out first and boldly said something sweet in just a few sentences and backed off. Up stepped this Vice President of the Academy of Sciences of USSR, and translated. He may have merely said what I should have said.

Well, that broadcast went out. They sent it on all the lines of the Russian radio system, so everybody would know we had come. Half an hour later we got to our hotel, which was near the Red Square. It was a newish hotel. We had been there only a little while when they moved us around. They found that I was the Führer, and so I had a room with a bath.

I was in my bathroom trying to find out which faucets would work and which would not. (None of them worked, so that was democratic enough.) I was stripped to the waist to take a little wash-up when there was a bang, Bang, BANG on my door. "Oh, gosh," I thought, "the G.P.U. or whatever they call it. Somebody has come. They've got on to me already." In Teheran we had been told that there might be all sorts of difficulties in Russia. I shouted "Come in." No answer. I shouted again, "Here I am!" and I spoke in what few languages I could use, inviting the knocker to come in. Finally, I went out, opened the hall door, and there stood a tallish, handsome young woman. I was bowled over. I thought, "This is one of those traps we hear about."

"Yes?" I said. "What is it?"

And in very good English she said, "I'm Zdenka. Here is your letter," holding out a letter. It was the one I had written on the Equator coming up from Capetown, about five years before.

"I didn't post my letter," I claimed. I was still confused and a bit scared. "Well, what are you doing here? You can't be Zdenka Kadla because she is at Omsk or somewhere a thousand miles to the east."

"I am here in the university," she said. "I heard you on the radio. I knew you were coming and so I got on my bicycle, and came in immediately to make contact with my pen pal."

I said, "Well, let me introduce you to the people at the desk. It will be safer."

So we went down to the desk. She had gone past it, apparently, on the way up. I told the hotel people, "She speaks English."

"Does she speak good English?" they asked.

I said, "Yes, very good English."

"Well, then we will ask her to be the guide for the Americans who are here with this delegation."

And so she had walked right into it. I asked her, "Well, now, Miss Kadla, just what are you doing at the university?"

"I'm studying astronomy," she said.

Another life that I had distorted! She was studying astronomy because I had described it, coming up from South Africa.

She took our delegation around and made a hit with us all. Professor A. A. Mikhailov, who was the leading astronomer of Russia at that time—he was head of the geodetic work, I believe, rather than astronomy—was glad that Zdenka could take care of us. I invited her to a cocktail party that was given by Ambassador W. Averell Harriman. We had a very gay party. Zdenka met champagne for the first time in her life and said she liked it. Somehow that annoyed me; people in Russia should not like champagne.

Zdenka showed us around the museums. They would not let her go up to Leningrad at that time, but she could do other things, and she was very useful. She was there up to the last day; then she had to go with Mikhailov and half a dozen other astronomers to see an eclipse. "Good-by, and thank you, and so forth, and we may renew our conversations as pen pals sometime."

Three years later, in 1948, the International Astronomical Union had a meeting at Zurich, Switzerland. I had telegraphed to the Russians: they had to send a delegation to Zurich if they wanted to keep their membership on international committees. I was not an officer, but I could act like one. They came, but as usual a day late, as they did for quite a number of years, because of red tape, I suppose. The Russian officials had gradually got on to the fact that there is no great risk in astronomers getting together. Anyway, there were eight Russians in Zurich, a day late. I knew several of them. "Hello, Kukarkin. Hello, Parenago. Happy to see you; glad you could come. And here comes Mikhailov." "Yes," said he, "I am here, Dr. Shapley. I am glad to see you also here. I have brought you a gift"—taking from his bag a bottle of cognac —"a gift from Zdenka."

"Well, isn't that nice! Zdenka Kadla remembers me. That is wonderful! Will you thank Zdenka?"

"Yes," he said, "I will thank Zdenka for you—that is, I will thank for you Mrs. Mikhailov!"

Mikhailov is the director of the Pulkovo Observatory, and Zdenka Mikhailov is the First Lady of Pulkovo. That concludes the story of Zdenka Kadla. It all came from writing letters on the Equator.

In the role of wandering scientist I have done a few things—a bit in Russia, as I have intimated, in England, and especially in India. I was in India three times giving lectures. On the first trip I met Pandit Nehru, who was greatly interested in science. He was the president of the Science Congress in India, which corresponds to the AAAS in America. The night I was elected president of the AAAS I flew across the ocean on my way to India. Nehru was not a professional scientist; he was a wise politician. But he knew science somewhat, too, and that drew us together. Later he came to see me in America. The last two or three times I saw him in India he was especially interested in the birth-control problem.

In New Delhi I gave a course of lectures to the scientists. They have some good young astronomers, mostly mathematical. Their equipment is almost zero; they are not accustomed to using instruments. They have no big telescopes, though we have been hearing for years that they are about to get some. The Australians sent a radio telescope to Delhi. That was a good international gesture. I was in India four or five years after it had arrived, and it had still not been unpacked. There was nobody then in India who was interested in carrying on that kind of research. To me that was shocking, but it does happen. After the First World War, we sent a number of beautiful German instruments, German optics, to Italy, as one of Germany's penalties for losing the war. For a long time the Italians didn't unpack them. Of course, they had other things to do.

Another international adventure is the Mexican one. I have been in Mexico six times, beginning in 1932 when I went for my "health." I studied the ants of Mexico, and went to the pelota games, and became fascinated with the country. Then, about 1941, I got interested in Mexico directly because a good amateur astronomer was the Mexican diplomatic secretary in Washington. He wanted us to build astronomy in Mexico where they had traditions and suitable climate and nothing else. Soon the Harvard Observatory was organizing the astronomers of the U.S.A. for a trip to Mexico. We were to go and build a new observatory. Harvard would do most of the building. We had at that time quite a staff that could help. Telescopes were designed, a site was chosen, thirty astronomers were lined up from all over the U.S.A. Everything was going well. I was traveling out in the West, I remember, and then came Pearl Harbor! I thought, "That ends it. We won't have any more of this worry of building telescopes for Mexico." But I was run to earth by that amateur Mexican diplomat-astronomer. He reported: "By all means we must go on with the astronomy and with the big plan you have for an observatory in Mexico. By all means we must do it. We'll provide the funds. I telephoned President Avila Camacho in the night. He said: 'Telescopes! We shall pay.'"

They did provide the funds, and we organized the astronomers. About thirty of us went down to dedicate the observatory and had a party for a week or two. Three of the telescopes were Harvard instruments that had been sent down on loan.

When the observatory was dedicated, the war was of course going on, but President Camacho said, "This is the best time in the world to emphasize the cultural solidarity of the Western Hemisphere." Here were astronomers taking a part in politics that they had not known they could do. It was a marvelous thing in many ways. I can get angry or joyous or amused about it. One thing that disturbed me was that when we assembled for the dedication of this beautiful observatory on a beautiful site, at Tonanzintla, east of the two great volcanoes, the natives came, the Indians came, and all the diplomatic corps came over to Tonanzintla from Mexico City—all except one diplomatic corps, and that was the United States. The United States ambassador had his instructions, I suppose.

The Americans sat around on the outside and looked on at the colorful event, and maybe made some notes about what was going on. It was embarrassing to us, but our State Department seems to be very clever at making boners.

I went down to Mexico again the next year; that time I took the physicists and the year after the mathematicians. By that time collaboration had become a habit, and ever since the United States and Mexico have had good connections in mathematics, in physics, and in astronomy. The American Physical Society met in Mexico in 1950. The connections there have been developed through the central government; I was of course decorated with top-notch Mexican honors—quite unnecessary.

Mexico is a charming place to go for astronomy. Two times out of three, if you take the proper medication, you don't get the national malady.

Chapter Ten

SCIENCE AND POLITICS

My first experience in the kind of activity that requires getting bills through Congress was in connection with the formation, in the 1940s, of the National Science Foundation, which I referred to earlier.

The National Science Foundation was built up as a government organization and it had many troubles in getting founded. James B. Conant, Kirtley F. Mather, and I were appointed, at the 1946 Boston meeting of the American Association for the Advancement of Science, as a committee to look into the possibility of getting government money for scientific research. One of the first things we did was to get various professional societies to endorse the operation. About seventy-five different organizations went on record in favor of the advisability of the government's giving money for research in science. The chairman was to be Dr. Arthur L. Day, president of Cornell, who accepted the job but then became ill. That put me, as vice-chairman, in charge, and I worked vigorously. We got a bill written; it had to be revised. We had good Congressmen; some of them were very willing and eager to work, but we fought over minor details. There was concern that funds might be given to the social sciences. Our survey of the seventy-five or so societies had showed that they were in favor of money going to the social sciences as well as to the natural sciences. That gesture of amity came from the natural scientists themselves.

The bill was partly through Congress, and then it was

killed. We tried again with some changes, and that bill was vetoed. Finally a bill went through. We did not offend Congress, and it was in favor of us. We asked for about $15 million to start with and settled for $2 million or $3 million. Times have changed—now the funds are in hundreds of millions. An enormous sum is being spent for scientific research. At first the scientific camel got only its nose under the tent; then the whole camel got in. The whole affair was indeed interesting. I was very active in this for a time; then I did not need to be any longer. A man who played a big part in it, not always in the open either, was Vannevar Bush, president of the Carnegie Institution of Washington. He and I had a session on what kind of person we should have to direct this affair. I knew what he thought, and so I decided to think the same thing: I proposed Alan T. Waterman, who was the head of OSRD. Bush agreed; it was one time that Vannevar Bush and I were in agreement. We both thought that Waterman, with the experience he had had in other organizations, would be good for this one. And so it was. Waterman remained director until he retired in 1963.

My next entanglement with politics was over UNESCO.

In 1945, toward the end of the Second World War, the diplomats were getting together in San Francisco to write the United Nations Charter. James Marshall, the former president of the New York City Board of Education, came to me and said in effect, "Would you go along with me and a few others in trying to get the delegates in San Francisco to put education in as a part of the charter?" We worked on it for quite some time. We wrote letters and tried to convince Congressmen. We also tried to convince the State Department —that was the main block—to let us announce that this was the program that we wanted to get through, in order to get some opinions on it. In other words, this was public relations in a big way. I think some of my stuff was ghost-written, or else I wasn't very wise when I wrote it. Anyway we published articles. We wanted to have a simple, harmless sort of resolution passed by both houses of Congress unanimously, saying: "We believe that education should be an important factor." But the State Department would not let us actually write a resolution or bill. The State Department was involved because it initiates international affairs. They thought we were just internationalists acting prematurely. The House of Representatives could not touch such a resolution if the State Department was against it, because the State Department was arranging for the continuity of civilization.

We went to see various people concerned with the United Nations, and we saw our Congressmen. The resolution we finally wrote was very harmless, but it was one that could start UNESCO. We followed a rather well-known custom: you write out the resolution that you want put through and take it to your favorite member of Congress but you include some errors in it, or at least one error, something that he can put his finger on and say, "No, not that." "Oh, all right, sir." Then he crosses out the error and it becomes his bill. The man who actually came to our aid was Representative (later Senator) Karl Mundt of South Dakota.

Finally, when the delegates were meeting in San Francisco, the State Department or some clerk in the State Department was authorized to say, "Well, if that Marshall-Shapley bunch wants to do this, I don't think it will do any harm." They did not quite say, "Go ahead and do it," but somebody said it wouldn't hurt. That was the signal to us to plunge ahead, and we plunged.

Eventually we had the hearings in the House, and we got

the resolution through unanimously. They had nothing to lose because they would not be responsible. The Senate would be.

The resolution was turned over to the Senate. I would have liked to be there, but Marshall did the job. The clerk read off the bill. The resolution was only a dozen lines or so. We had written in the protection that no country could control the education of another. Apparently it was going through and all looked well, when up comes a patriot. "Wait, wait," he said. "Is this the business that the Senator from Arkansas [J. William Fulbright] and Mr. Taft were talking to me about in the cloakroom?" "Yes," someone said. "Oh, all right," he said and sat down. The resolution went through without opposition.

We at once got Archibald MacLeish on the telephone in San Francisco. We told MacLeish, who was Assistant Secretary of State, and at the UN meetings, about our success, read the resolution to him, and said, "Now put it through the UN." That was the birth of what became UNESCO.

As soon as the resolution got through Congress we had to decide what name the organization should have. The people in San Francisco, especially MacLeish, argued that putting "science" in the name would make it too long. "United Nations Educational and Cultural Organization will take in all the sciences and the engineers." I blew up. I telephoned MacLeish across the country from the sculptor Jo Davidson's laboratory-museum in New York, and said, "We have to have science represented in the title of the operation. I am going to get action from the scientists' groups. And we are going to have an international organization in science. We're experienced. We've had dozens and dozens of international operations."

"But," said MacLeish, "people won't stand for such a long name."

"Well," I said, "let's try it out. Go out on Telegraph Hill or wherever you are and ask the first person you see, 'Is chemical engineering an art or a culture?' He'll say, 'No, it's a science.' "

"I shall try," he said sadly, "to put it through."

Within a few weeks I was one of a dozen Americans chosen by the State Department to go to London to write the charter of UNESCO. There was some difficulty about a passport for me because I was a "dangerous character," and rather proud of it. My selection went through because Mrs. Gunnar Myrdal, the Swedish delegate to the UNESCO conference, asked that I be sent by our State Department.

Writing the charter took only two or three weeks. We spelled out what UNESCO could do and how it should be done. I was the official American scientist on the job. The sessions were beautifully managed by MacLeish. I would not have thought a poet and librarian could do it so well. We wrote the charter in fine language. It begins: "Since wars begin in the minds of men it is in the minds of men that the defenses of peace must be constructed"—a beautiful expression. Poet MacLeish was given full credit for it, but actually Prime Minister Clement Attlee first said "Wars begin in the minds of men." It is a lovely sort of preface.

The mid-1940s was the time when scientists first realized that they needed to organize in order to have a voice in politics. The atomic scientists organized to have a voice in the peacetime uses of atomic energy, and the Federation of American Scientists was formed. At the same time we had to scrap against the House Un-American Activities people. The Condon affair came along, and later the Oppenheimer scandal. The scientists were awakening, but also they were awakening the opposition.

I was in on the founding of the Federation of American Scientists—it had two or three earlier names, but that is what it was finally called. I am still on the advisory council, but I haven't been active for several years, because we have done the job—namely, getting scientists into government bureaus. My second son, Alan Shapley, was also a leader in the Federation, but he isn't a member any more. He says, "We did what we set out to do." In the beginning he worked on it a great deal, taking much time away from his scientific research.

During this same period—1946-1947, to be exact—I had a run-in with the House Un-American Activities Committee. John Rankin of Mississippi was chairman at the time. The affair got a lot of newspaper publicity: "Dr. Harlow Shapley charged tonight that his subpoena by the House Un-American Activities Committee was 'an obvious political maneuver' to discredit the work of all independent voters" (*New York Times,* November 4, 1946). Then there were headlines: "Rankin clashes with Dr. Shapley." "Un-American Committee man charges contempt. Scientist alleges Gestapo hearing."

The way all this came about was that Joseph Martin from Massachusetts, who was House leader, was running for re-election and a Unitarian lady, Mrs. Martha Sharp, was running against him. It was supposed to be completely silly for anybody to try to upset Joe Martin. But here she came, and she was making a good deal of headway, though she did not have much money for the campaign. I remember calling up her house once and a little girl, about six years old, answered: "Martha Sharp for President." I was of course pro-Martha Sharp.

At that time I was connected with the National Council of the Arts, Sciences and Professions. It was a straight liberal operation; it was not even called Communist. The organization raised money for various campaigns. One was against Joe Martin. The NCASP sent money to Martha Sharp to help her in her campaign for Congress. Of course she got beaten; the politicians were very rough with her. She got beaten partly because Joe Martin appealed to John Rankin, his chum in Congress: "They are making quite a fuss about me; can't you get your hounds after them?" Whereupon, deliberately, Rankin sent one or two of his men to look into the situation in this Massachusetts district.

Naturally they got to work on the business of smearing Martha Sharp. She's a wonderful lady but not too good as a politician. She had worked a good deal for Unitarian relief organizations. These agents for the politicians burglarized Mrs. Sharp's office. Among other things, they found a letter I had written to Martha Sharp—a virtuous letter, to the effect that: "If you want us to help you, you certainly should be willing to state where the money comes from." For political reasons she did not want to admit that the money came from us, but she needed the money.

When they got hold of my letter they had a name. That was the main thing they wanted. I have been useful in one way—by having a name known to scoundrels. That was all they needed. They got scareheads into the newspapers: "Shapley protects the Communists" and the like. Whereupon, as a part of the machinery, one of Rankin's agents came to see me in my office. I said, "I won't talk to you without a lawyer present because I don't trust you." I knew that man.

Zachariah Chaffee, Harvard Law School, a liberal, came to represent me in an interview. He was asked very leading questions, but we felt we had been rather successful in confronting these agents of the red-hunters.

But no. They went back to Washington and pretty soon came a subpoena for me to come down there. I said, "I won't go unless I can have the assurance that I can have a lawyer there."

Rankin said, "You won't need a lawyer. It's just a matter of finding out about this letter." Still, I thought it was understood that I would have a lawyer on hand. But Zach Chaffee got ill and couldn't go. He sent instead a man who is now chancellor of Washington University in St. Louis, Dr. Thomas Eliot. Tom Eliot had been in Congress, and in Congress he had had a scrap with Rankin, so they knew each other. Tom said he would go down instead of Zach Chaffee.

That is the only time I have ever had need of a lawyer. It was one of these Star Chamber affairs, with only one committee man present. There were two or three of his sleuths, or whatever you want to call them, but no other Congressmen. We protested, but we went into the hearing. In the anteroom were a lot of newspaperman with flash guns poised. Finally Rankin came in. When he saw Tom he shouted, "You get out of here."

I protested, "But I have been given a promise I could have my lawyer."

"You could have had that lawyer you mentioned, but here you bring this lawyer. Zach Chaffee, yes, but Eliot, no!" The fact that Chaffee was ill and couldn't come gave them an out.

I said, "I cannot go on without him." But some way or other they maneuvered Tom Eliot into the anteroom with the reporters and started questioning me alone. I had brought with me my secretary, a little blonde. I asked her if she had taken a note on something, and that stirred up Rankin again.

"Who is that woman?"

I said, "She is here with me. We are keeping a record."

"You don't need to do that. We'll give you a record of anything you ought to know."

I said, "It would be only what I ought to know from your viewpoint, sir . . ."

"Throw her out!" he shouted.

And out she went, this little blonde girl, scared to death, of course, because this Congressman seemed such a ruffian.

I said, "Very well, if she can't be here, I'll be my own recorder." I have mentioned that I write shorthand. I started to write down all that was being said. That made him even madder. He came crawling over the intervening table and grabbed the notes out of my hand. I rose in my great dignity and said, "This is a case of assault."

But that did not bother Rankin. He said, "You are going to be cited for contempt of Congress."

I get compliments; sometimes I fish for them. Here was an opportunity. I came out into the anteroom—flash, flash, flash, flash: the newspaper people were there. And out also came Congressman Rankin. He came out, pointing his scornful finger at me, and shouted, "This man has shown more contempt for our committee than anybody who ever appeared before it." That was the greatest compliment I had ever had. It was flattering to be held in contempt of that committee.

The Democratic party manager tried to get Rankin to withdraw the contempt charge, because they saw it would be an uphill fight. Finally the charge was squelched.

The Southern newspapers jumped onto Rankin in brilliant fashion. One said, "If jittery John wants to get head-lines, have him crawl to the top of the Washington Monument and jump off. He'll get headlines." That was a Jackson, Mississippi, paper, I think. The Richmond newspapers also went after him. The Southern press was noble in this case.

It was all rather tough on my nerves. I had lunch with President Conant. He does not understand Congressmen. But he didn't fire me! When I went home I found that the students—1200 of them—had put out a manifesto *for* Mr. Shapley. "Members of the Harvard Liberal Union presented Dr. Harlow Shapley a pledge carrying 1200 signatures to back up his 'courageous stand against the action of the committee.'" The Harvard undergraduate population was about 4300 at the time. We had a meeting to celebrate; Dr. Bok took a noble part in the enterprise. To have 1200 Harvard students signing a paper indicating that they thought Dr. Shapley had done a good deed for humanity was *something*. Coming from Harvard students it was something tremendous, because they were then naturally conservative. Maybe some of them signed blindly.

The American Association of Scientific Workers also condemned the Rankin committee for its treatment of me. I was quite a martyr. Oddly enough, Rankin helped put through the Tennessee Valley Authority. But that is the only thing I ever heard to his credit.

J. Parnell Thomas of New Jersey, who succeeded Rankin as the chairman of the Un-American Activities Committee, was another character. The Wall Street people who lived on his side of the Hudson River kept voting for him because they thought he was "amusing." His real name was Feeney, or some such good Irish name. He was pretty effective, but he was finally put in jail for graft and passed out of the political scene.

At the same time James Michael Curley in Boston was making merry at the expense of Kirtley Mather, Harlow Shapley, and a few others. These politicians had decided that the best thing they could do to get re-elected was to get more antagonisms going. Curley was mayor of Boston and a Congressman at the same time; he also was soon in jail for graft. He was a man with abilities and skill. They used to say in Washington, "Politics in Boston is either straight or Curley."

Another time that I had some unwanted publicity in connection with the National Association of the Arts, Sciences, and Professions was in March 1949, when we had several big peace meetings in New York City and some Russian musicians and poets came over. We had quite a wild party— we later called it the Waldorf Operation. There were pickets at the hotel and on Fifth Avenue. It became a disgraceful affair from the standpoint of the newspapers. The New York *Sun* in its earlier editions came out very much for me and against the other New York papers. Before the later editions the editors on the *Sun* saw that I was to be the goat, the one to be challenged. They just changed hats between editions, from Shapley being the great man to Shapley being a heel.

In 1947, shortly after the Rankin affair, I was elected president of the American Association for the Advancement of Science. I succeeded Conant. Since we were both at Harvard and lived within a few blocks of each other, I thought it was a bit of a miscarriage that I was elected then. But I was, and part of the reason was that many people wanted to show the red-hunters that scientists don't pay any attention to them in a matter of this kind.

I think my troubles with Rankin and that type of political hack were an asset in the Association. In the heavy correspondence I don't remember more than one or two letters that said, "Don't you want to resign?" or some such inquiry. I think that the members of the AAAS looked at it the same way that Harvard did, with respect to a professor under attack by the red-hunters. Harvard would go out of the way to say "We don't elect to act the way you want us to act. We're talking about science."

There was another amusing matter. John Ciardi, the poet, later an editor on the *Saturday Review,* and I were attacked by a man in Baltimore named Frank B. Ober. He wouldn't give any money to the Harvard Law School, which was soliciting money, until Harvard fired Shapley and Ciardi. It turned out on investigation that he had never heard either of us speak a word. He was getting headlines. Ober wrote to President Conant, who asked Grenville Clark, the senior member of the Harvard Corporation which owns and runs Harvard, to answer the letter. Clark wrote quite a famous statement on the meaning of academic freedom. I found out finally what I was worth to Harvard. Maybe the figure was inflated. It sounds rather funny nowadays. "Mr. Ober," Clark said in his letter, which was published in the *Harvard Alumni Bulletin,* June 25, 1949, "if you had offered us $5 million for the discharge of Mr. Shapley, you wouldn't lose any money."

Having become a target for the red-hunters, I naturally was not neglected by Senator Joseph McCarthy. I never met him face to face, but he went after me publicly twice. Once was in a famous speech in Reno, Nevada, when I was named by him as one of half a dozen Communists in the State Department. (Not only was I not a Communist, I had no connection with the State Department!) The Associated Press crashed through that time. Sometimes those people do nice things. They woke me up in the middle of the night at the Harvard Club in New York City and said, "McCarthy has just made the following statement," and they read it off. I did a double take and said, "I have heard the statement by Senator McCarthy to the Associated Press, and I have only to say that the Senator succeeded in telling six lies in four sentences, which is probably the indoor record for mendacity." That squelched McCarthy. He kept off me after that until Mr. Conant wanted to go to Germany as ambassador. At that time McCarthy asked him why he didn't fire Harlow Shapley, and Conant said, "That isn't the way we do things."

A newspaper story in *The New York Times*, March 15, 1950, quotes me as saying that McCarthy's allegations were untrue and vague, that I was "as far from being a Communist as possible" and that I found McCarthy's irresponsible charges tiresome and would like him to get more specific. Then it goes on: "The astronomer said he had 'an ace up my sleeve' if the Senator did become specific in his accusations. He then added that 'If it comes to a fight, I shall speak out strongly and fearlessly.' He did not elaborate on the ace he professed to hold." I wish I could remember what ace I had up my sleeve—I have a suspicion that I was bluffing. There was a good deal of tumbling around in those days.

A different mixture of politics with science was my association with Henry A. Wallace. I knew Wallace over a good many years because of his work in the Department of Agriculture and his other scientific interests. He was the type of person—a lot of people said this—who might not have been very astute politically but as a scientist and a human being he was an uncommonly remarkable man. His father before him had built up a fortune out in Iowa with the publication *Wallace's Farmer*. I heard not long ago that the fortune was once lost and Henry Wallace went back to Iowa and restored it.

The first time I met Wallace was when we were both broadcasting on the twentieth birthday of Science Service in 1941. E. G. Conklin, Princeton biologist and my predecessor as president of Science Service, was also there, and Watson Davis and others. Wallace and I stood around and talked quite a while about genetics before we made the broadcast. He was then Vice President. During the course of that discussion I happened to mention that the following week I was going to Mexico on the job I have described of helping build up Mexican science.

"Do you speak Spanish?" asked Mr. Wallace.

I said, "No, I'm not that kind. I'm not as good as you are, speaking so many languages you can go to any country."

He said, "Well, I'll teach you how to learn Spanish easily."

"How is that, Mr. Wallace?"

"We sing it. We sing popular songs. Come out to my house tonight," he said, "and bring Mrs. Shapley."

We went out to his apartment. His wife was away at a meeting of some sort. He got out some Spanish records and sang along in what I call his "whiskey tenor." He asked me then to come out another time. He said, "I'd like to have you tell my deputy secretary that there's nothing to astrology, that it's just nonsense, and he shouldn't talk about planting things down in Mexico or Central America in the light of the moon. I want you to bug him if you will."

Sure enough, at a later dinner, Wallace maneuvered the conversation so that pretty soon I was listening to water divining, astrology, and such. Apparently I did all right, for that man quieted down about planting potatoes in the light of the moon. This man was Wallace's second in command, so it was important not to have him appear publicly foolish. Many people thought that Wallace himself was an astrologer and a visionary in all sorts of ways. But I know that he was hardheaded. Hadn't he built up a considerable fortune?

Because he did not present himself very well, it has been usual to say that Wallace would have done much better as a college professor, because he knew so much and had such wide interests. I went to see him while he was Secretary of Agriculture, to ask if he could use influence to get released from the Air Force one genius-type scientific youth who was needed for a very definite reason—the study of multiple ovulation in cattle. He explained that because of the political set-up it couldn't be done.

Our conference was an interesting session. I went into his front office and there, waiting, were two United States Senators. I recognized one of them and later identified the other. Wallace's staff had a list of the people who were to come in. Quite out of order I was ushered into his office. That rather startled me. Since I don't like special favors, I protested a bit. The office girl said, "No, he wants you to come now." I went in and there he was, tired, worked to death. Did he want to talk to me about my job or about agriculture or ovulation or about the government? No, he wanted details about certain researches that were going on in science. I told him about the ionization in cool stars, or something of that kind. He was doodling while I was talking to him, so I stopped; he asked me to go on. I was a little bit offended at the doodling. He called attention to something on his desk, and I stepped over to look. I saw "Fe_2O_5." He was writing down the chemical formulas I was talking about. The reason he wanted me there and put me ahead of Senators was to have a chance to save his soul from politics. So I stayed with him quite a while. I felt exhilarated by his knowing these chemical symbols. Many a geneticist and many a Senator does not know that Fe means iron.

I had dinner with Wallace near the time of the death of Franklin D. Roosevelt. Wallace was a good sport. After he lost the vice-presidential nomination in 1944 by a narrow margin, he immediately offered his services to FDR to do whatever he could politically in the campaign. FDR chose to have a big rally in Madison Square Garden in New York at which I presided. There were some 20,000 people there. Wallace was on the program. I introduced him and some of the radio comedians. We had a group from Hollywood and raised a good deal of money for the general campaign. I had already had some experience in presiding at the Madison Square Garden type of meeting. This was a good one.

After that I didn't see Wallace for a while except at the meetings of the American Philosophical Society, of which he was a member. Since the time of Thomas Jefferson or maybe Woodrow Wilson, no politician had been in that sacred institution, but as an agriculturist and a hybrid-corn man, Wallace was elected on his merits as a scientist to that society.

In 1948 Wallace ran for President on the Progressive party ticket. The Progressive party held its convention in Philadelphia. They wanted me to come to it, but that was obviously just to use my name rather than for any official service I could perform. So I was not there officially, but I happened to stop in Philadelphia on my way back from the South at the time that the convention was going on. Wallace had an apartment there. I visited with him and Mrs. Wallace and one or two friends, including the labor leader from the West Coast, Harry Bridges. I was with Wallace when the convention was voting against him—it amounted to that. In platform making they had got to the place where they should have disclaimed fascism and other isms. They didn't do it. The Communists climbed aboard the bandwagon and manipulated the vote for the so-called Vermont resolution, and Wallace went along. He thought that it was the intelligent and moral thing to do. He accepted a platform that did not spank the Communists; he should have spanked them at that moment. The Communists controlled the convention.

I pulled out then. But Wallace stayed with the Commies and lost three or four million votes. In fact, he did not get quite a million. Even though I couldn't go along with the party, I voted for Wallace; in fact, at the time of the election I was in Boulder, Colorado, and I made a special effort to have my vote transmitted. I was pro-Wallace at that time—pro-Wallace but anti-party.

From that time most of our association was again through the American Philosophical Society. I often sat with him at the dinners and talked corn and politics. Mrs. Wallace used to come also. They enjoyed the meetings very much because Wallace had been left behind in the political scramble, and, you might also say, in the social scramble. But to be a member of the American Philosophical Society in his own right seemed to appeal to him, though in the last few years of his life he did not go often to its meetings. He once gave a technical paper on genetics. Wallace was getting along pretty well on hybridizing chickens. He managed to breed the ugliest chicken you ever saw, but the goal was realized—more return per ounce of feed.

In 1965 I heard that Wallace was ill. So I dropped him a note, wishing him well, and could he come over and see my son Carl's school? He wrote that he expected to be better very soon and then would be so happy to have me over to his place. The answer really indicated that he was on the way out.

I wrote him a long letter and told him all the news about the various mutual friends of early times. That probably was the last letter he received. Very soon afterward he died. His wife wrote me later to express her appreciation of my cheering him up at such a time.

There are many nice things to say about Henry Wallace, the things he represented and the courage that he gave to other people. He was a truly great American. But he should have been cast as a professional scientist or a teacher, rather than as a statesman.

Chapter Eleven

A SUMMING UP

When I look back over the various things I have done, there are certain high points, and of course a few regrets. I have always wished that I had really learned chemistry. It was a mistake of mine that I did not get more chemistry and less Latin, although I have enjoyed the Latin. And I would like to have been better trained in mathematical astronomy. But I was too busy with research. I have made other mistakes in getting educated, and I am not yet very well educated.

While I have written a considerable number of books other than technical, scientific volumes, I always think they are poorly done, with one or two exceptions. I claim that I have not written anything that I would accept if I were an instructor in English at Harvard University.

But outstanding among my writings is an essay called "A Design for Fighting." That was originally a talk that I gave in Cleveland during the Second World War; I was representing Phi Beta Kappa in a meeting of the American Association for the Advancement of Science, and I was expected to give a talk of the sort that William James might have given long ago. He gave a lecture and an argument on much the same theme that was part of my own inspiration. I suggested that the real enemies we should fight are disease, poverty, hate, ignorance, and suspicion.

An interesting aspect of my lecture was that when I delivered it I got practically no applause. I think it is one of the best I have done, but no one in the audience said it was any good at all, except two girls who had both been on my computing staff!

As an essay it has been reprinted many times. Within a short time it appeared in the *Atlantic Monthly*, the *American Scholar*, and the *American Scientist* and has since appeared in several anthologies and in my own book *The View from a Distant Star* (1963). I don't know whether it has had much effect, but it is still referred to occasionally. I once thought that I should write an article on its twenty-fifth anniversary, calling it the "Anniversary of 'Design for Fighting.'" But I did not do it; I had more important things to do.

Later I put a good deal of the same thought into a little book called *Of Stars and Men* (1958). That has now been published in eight languages, and as a paperback, and has been made into a movie by John Hubley and Faith Eliot. It was not too well done. When I had a chance, on a second revision, I changed many phrases around. I believe that book went over well because a voice of some authority (mine) was saying what other people were thinking. But it is a little odd that it was published in Hindi and Polish and various other uncommon languages. The Hindi copy went to Pandit Nehru, and he wrote me a little note while he was traveling, saying that he liked it. I don't know whether he actually "cracked" the book or not, but anyway he made that nice statement.

Writing used to come easy to me because as a newspaper reporter I had to write fast. It was imperative. But as I have grown older, I don't write as well, it seems to me, and I have to go over a manuscript many times. I don't have good self-discipline. I should have forced myself to write well from the first.

Among my achievements outside astronomy, I have collaborated in producing a rather remarkable family. In my international operations, a high spot was when Pandit Nehru, visiting Harvard, asked President Conant to let him go to the Observatory to see Doctor Shapley.

Astronomy has changed so rapidly in recent years, on account of the invasion of space science, that my astronomy of the 1920s has become old-fashioned and I am at times embarrassed about it, even though I do know some things and can talk fast enough to get away with being ignorant.

Back in 1900 there were distinguished American astronomers such as E. C. Pickering, Simon Newcomb, and W. W. Campbell. They were very good astronomers for their day, but with what they knew then none of them could now pass elementary astronomy at Harvard University, or at most other colleges. The science has gone far beyond them and away from them; different techniques are involved. For instance, the *Astrophysical Journal* is now almost wholly mathematics and astrophysics, written by authors whose names are completely unknown to me. We have been forced with the advance of technology, and especially of space science, to use a bigger and wider brush. Radio astronomy is one of the big things that now dominates. It started rather mildly, first with amateur astronomers and then with physicists getting into the act. Finally the professional astronomers caught on, and the field really expanded.

A great advantage nowadays is that one can get money for scientific research in much larger chunks than you could in an earlier time. I used to boast about how much money I had raised for Harvard. It was a few million dollars, obtained in one way or another for astronomy, biology, physics, and so forth. Now when they talk about Harvard's having an endowment of a billion dollars, that looks like small potatoes.

In the scientific way, I suppose my number one contribution was locating the center of our galaxy some 33,000 or more light-years from the sun; in other words, the "overthrow" of the heliocentric hypothesis of Copernicus. The sun-centered universe is dead and has been dead ever since the plots of the distribution of globular star clusters were developed on the basis of the pulsating theory of the Cepheid variables. Several colleagues have helped in the "overthrow," of course.

Then, too, before the Cepheid variable star type of study was developed, we could measure only a distance of a hundred light-years with much certainty; after that we could measure a million. Going from a hundred light-years to a million gives us a new view of the universe and a grasp of the size of the galaxy.

But I realize that, as with so many other discoveries, if I had not made them, probably some other discoverer would have come along and reaped the credit. That happens so often in science. Suppose that Carl D. Anderson at California Institute of Technology hadn't made his positron identification when he did; somebody else would have. In fact, one worker now claims he would have had it four weeks later. Discovery was just that close. That's the way it is with a good deal of the work I have done.

Of the various fields I have worked in, many yielded results that are right: I haven't made many mistakes—only a few blunders, not many.

I got the direction to the center of the galaxy correctly

within a degree or two—spotted from the distribution of giant variables and the globular star clusters and novae. Three other methods of getting the direction to the center of our galaxy have been found, and they yield results within a degree or so of my value. So I hit that nail on the head all right. But I was not accurate as to the distance. I first guessed the distance at 50,000 light-years, and I whittled that down to 25,000 and then revised it up to 30,000. We are still working on the distance to the center. I thought I had good evidence for my first values, but I had overlooked something that I should not have overlooked. I ignored the absorption of light in space.

Not so long ago, when I was going down a street in Harvard Square I met a dean, who stopped me and said, in effect, "It is your turn to entertain the Exam Club. Your paper is slated for next Monday."

"Oh, no," I said, "things are not going well. I have nothing to contribute. I don't know anything. Why do you say it is my turn?"

"Because it is your turn. All you have to do now is to give me the title of what you are going to talk about and I shall send out the notices. That will give you time to do some useful thinking."

"All right. I will do it since I must do it. And the title of my talk can well be: 'The Scientific Blunders I Have Made.' "

"Oh, no," said the dean. "Not that; it is only to be a one-hour program."

CHRONOLOGY

SELECTED BIBLIOGRAPHY

INDEX

Chronology

1885 Harlow Shapley born November 2, Nashville, Missouri.

1901 Becomes newspaper reporter, first in Chanute, Kansas, later in Joplin, Missouri.

1907 Graduates from Carthage Collegiate Institute, Carthage, Missouri; enters the University of Missouri.

1910 A. B., University of Missouri.

1911 A. M., University of Missouri; receives the Thaw Fellowship in astronomy at Princeton University; begins graduate study at Princeton under Henry Norris Russell.

1913 Ph.D., Princeton University; first European trip; father killed by lightning.

1914 Becomes astronomer at the Mount Wilson Observatory; marries Martha Betz, April 15.

1920 "The Great Debate" with Heber D. Curtis; held at the annual meeting of the National Academy of Science, Washington, D.C., April 26.

1921 Appointed Director of Harvard College Observatory and Paine Professor of Astronomy.

1926 Awarded Draper Medal of the National Academy of Sciences.

1927 LL.D., University of Missouri, the first of seventeen honorary degrees.

1928 Delivers the Halley Lecture at Oxford University, "The Search for the Centre of the Milky Way."

1931 Awarded medal of Society of Arts and Sciences for work in astronomy.

1932 Host to the Fourth General Assembly of the International Astronomical Union at Harvard.

1933 Receives honorary D.Sc. from both Princeton and Harvard; awarded Janssen prize of the French Astronomical Society and the Rumford Medals of the American Academy of Arts and Sciences.

1934 Awarded the gold medal of the Royal Astronomical Society.

1936   Presides at Harvard Tercentenary Astronomical Symposium.

1939   Elected President of the American Academy of Arts and Sciences; awarded Bruce Medal of the Astronomical Society of the Pacific.

1941   Awarded the Pope Pius XI Prize for astronomy.

1942   Speaks at the dedication of the Mexican national observatory at Tonanzintla.
         Initiates radio program sponsored by Harvard and World Wide Broadcasting Foundation; leads fight against government seizure of station WRUL.

1943   Delivers address at the commemoration of the 400th anniversary of the death of Copernicus and the publication of *De Revolutionibus*.

1945   Presents scroll to the Academy of Sciences of the USSR on the 220th anniversary of its founding; the first of three trips to Russia.

1946   Participates in the formation of UNESCO; investigated by the House Committee on Un-American Activities.

1947   Elected President of the American Association for the Advancement of Science; first trip to India.

1950   Attacked by Senator Joseph McCarthy.

1952   Retires as Director of the Harvard College Observatory.

Selected Bibliography

BY HARLOW SHAPLEY

Starlight. New York: George H. Doran Co., 1926.
Star Clusters. New York: McGraw-Hill Book Company, 1930
Flights from Chaos. New York: McGraw-Hill Book Company, 1930
Galaxies. Philadelphia: The Blakiston Company, 1943; rev. ed., Cambridge, Mass.: Harvard University Press, 1961
The Inner Metagalaxy. New Haven, Conn.: Yale University Press, 1957
Of Stars and Men. Boston: Beacon Press, 1958
The View from a Distant Star. New York: Basic Books, 1963
Beyond the Observatory. New York: Charles Scribner's Sons, 1967

EDITED BY HARLOW SHAPLEY

The Universe of Stars. Edited by Harlow Shapley and Cecilia H. Payne. Cambridge, Mass.: Harvard Observatory, 1926; rev. ed., 1929
A Source Book in Astronomy 1500-1900. Edited by Harlow Shapley and Helen E. Howarth. New York: McGraw-Hill Book Company, 1929
A Treasury of Science. Edited by Harlow Shapley, Samuel Rapport, and Helen Wright. New York: Harper & Brothers, 1943
Readings in the Physical Sciences. Edited by Harlow Shapley, Helen Wright, and Samuel Rapport. New York: Appleton-Century-Crofts, Inc., 1948
Climatic Change. Cambridge, Mass.: Harvard University Press, 1953
Science Ponders Religion. New York: Appleton-Century-Crofts, Inc., 1960
Source Book in Astronomy 1900-1950. Cambridge, Mass.: Harvard University Press, 1960
The New Treasury of Science. Edited by Harlow Shapley, Samuel Rapport, and Helen Wright. New York: Harper & Row, 1965

ABOUT HARLOW SHAPLEY

"Five Articles Honoring Harlow Shapley on His Eightieth Birthday," *Publications of the Astronomical Society of the Pacific*, 77 (October and December 1965): Peter van de Kamp, "The Galactocentric Revolution"; Helen Sawyer Hogg, "Harlow Shapley and Globular Clusters"; Carl Schalén, "On Some Problems of Interstellar Absorption"; Bart J. Bok, "Shapley's Researches on the Magellanic Clouds"; Hudson Hoagland, "Harlow Shapley—Some Recollections."

Index

(The page number *f. 52* indicates that the person or subject appears one or more times in the Illustrations section, which follows page 52 of the text.)

Adams, Walter S., 50, 51, *f. 52*, 55, 56, 58, 99
Agassiz, Alexander, 84
Agassiz, George Russell, 81, 84, 85
Agassiz, Louis, 84
Aller, Lawrence, 97
American Academy of Arts and Sciences, 120, 121, 122
American Association for the Advancement of Science (AAAS), 138, 155-156
American Association for Variable Star Observers (AAVSO), 91, 99
American Astronomical Society, 38, *f. 52*, 110
American Philosophical Society, 122, 161
American Physical Society, 141
Ames, Adelaide, *f. 52*, 103, 105
Anderson, Carl D., 168
ants, 65-72
Arequipa (Peru) Southern Station, 98, 101, 102
Aristotle, 35
asteroids, 55
Astronomical and Astrophysical Society of America, *see* American Astronomical Society
Astronomical Society of the Pacific, 89
Astronomische Gesellschaft, 42
Astronomy of the 20th Century, 79
Astrophysical Journal, 38, 167
Attlee, Clement, 149

Babcock, Harold D., 55
Bailey, Irving, 90
Bailey, Solon I., 41, 52, *f. 52*, 85, 90
Baker, James, 97, 129
Banachiewicz, T. H., 130, 131
Betz, Martha, *see* Shapley, Martha Betz
binaries, 35-37

Bishop, Morris, 11
Bok, Bart J., *f. 52*, 54, 96, 97, 115, 129, 130, 154
Boyden Station, Bloemfontein, South Africa, *f. 52*, 101, 102
Bridges, Harry, 161
British Astronomical Association, 95
Bronk, Detlev, 69
Bryson, Lyman, 113
Burhoe, Ralph, 115
Bush, Vannevar, 118, 146

Camacho, Avila, 140
Campbell, Leon, *f. 52*, 90
Campbell, W. W., 55, 167
Cannon, Annie J., 40, *f. 52*, 54, 85, 91-93, 102, 130, 131
Carmichael, Leonard, 118
Carthage Collegiate Institute, 12
Cepheid variable stars, 36, 39, 52, 53, 100, 168
Chaffee, Zachariah, 151, 152
Chanute (Kansas) *Daily Sun*, 9-10, 11, 23
Ciardi, John, 156
Clark, Grenville, 156
Columbia, Missouri, 17
Communists, 156, 161
Compton, Karl T., 34
Conant, James B., 129, 145, 154, 155, 156, 157, 167
Cone, Fred, 23
Conklin, E. G., 158
Conrad, Victor, 127
Coolidge, Julian, 93
Copernicus, 60, 131, 132, 168
Crandon, Margery, 122
Curley, James Michael, 155
Curtis, Heber D., *f. 52*, 61, 75, 76, 77, 79, 80

2284-20-14
69ρ
8/76